C000179547

# The
# Expatriate
# Siamese

BY THE SAME AUTHOR

*Enjoying Majorca*
*Illustrated by Claire Baker*

# The Expatriate Siamese

## By Pamela Legge

### Illustrated by Sally Holmes

**G G Baker & Associates**

# G G Baker & Associates

Saffron Hill, Chedworth, Glos. GL54 4AL
&
PO Box 1, 07184 Calviá, Mallorca, Spain

First published in Great Britain by G G Baker & Associates 2000

Copyright © Pamela Legge, 2000
Illustrations copyright © Sally Holmes, 2000

All rights reserved.
Without limiting the rights under copyright reserved above, no part of
this publication may be reproduced, stored in a database, retrieval
system, or web page without the prior written permission of both the
copyright owners and the publisher as listed above.

A catalogue record for this book is
available from the British Library

Printed and bound in Great Britain by Biddles Ltd, Guildford, Surrey

ISBN 0 906635 26 8

To my husband with thanks
for his support and patience
during the writing of this book,
and to Tia Maria for enriching
our lives for so many years.

# Contents

# 1. Mitzi

Earlier that morning, a thin layer of mist had obscured the coastal strip, leaving hillocks standing out like islands in a grey sea, but it had cleared quickly to reveal a calm blue Mediterranean and a cloudless sky.

The white buildings lining the south-west shore of Mallorca, highlighted by the brilliant sunshine, contrasted sharply with the green patchwork of almond orchards and olive groves covering the lower slopes of the mountains, while thousands of pines clung tenaciously to crevices in the rocks above.

However, the perfect day was marred for me because Graham was preparing for a trip to the UK. I lay on the bed, scrutinising every movement as he packed his suitcase and moaning involuntarily whenever I thought of his impending departure—although I was unable to fully express my feelings, he was aware of my absolute devotion.

By eavesdropping on a telephone conversation, I already knew that Graham had booked a return flight from Palma to Gatwick, but the purpose of his hastily arranged journey was wrapped in mystery. I had followed him into the bedroom in order to be near him for as long as possible before he left for the airport.

Instead of his usual informal garb, Graham was wearing a long-sleeved cream shirt, a pale blue silk tie, and grey trousers with knife-edged creases; a matching jacket was draped casually over the king-size bed, which dominated the room. Colourful rugs, some attractive watercolours, and a crystal chandelier relieved the stark white walls and plain tiled floor—typical of a Mallorquin house. The slatted *persianas* were closed against the midday sun but the wood-framed windows were wide open, allowing a pleasantly cool breeze to waft over my body.

I lay on the soft quilt, resting my head on a sleeve of Graham's jacket and nuzzling the material to savour the familiar scent of his cologne. When he leaned over to place two clean shirts into his suitcase, I stretched out seductively and lightly touched his arm.

He turned and looked at me sympathetically: 'I know darling—I'll miss you too, but I'll be back soon bringing something exciting for you,' he said as he slipped on his jacket and clicked the case shut.

Still moaning intermittently, I followed him down the stairs to the hall where his wife, Pam, was waiting to escort him to the car.

'Good-bye Tia, cheer up—I'll be home in two days,' he said, gently stroking my head.

I watched as he kissed Pam tenderly, promising to telephone that evening; then he waved to us as he drove off, the tyres of the car raising clouds of dust from the gravelled drive that had not seen rain for many weeks. It was July and the heat would be intense for the next two months. In our eyrie in the mountains above Calviá, the temperature is at least five degrees lower than on the plain, but even so I had to move quickly to avoid burning my feet on the hot tiles as I walked round to the shady terrace in search of a comfortable lounger.

My full name is Tia Maria but it is usually shortened to Tia. I am a chocolate-point Siamese with the perfect bone structure specified for my breed—an elegantly domed head, well-formed chin, lithe leopard-like body with high-set shoulder blades, and a long tail. The unusually soft fur of my body is predominantly cream, merging into café-au-lait on my lower legs and paws and a deeper brown on my mask, ears, and tail. My slightly pointed face features an imperious nose, large pricked ears—separated by a striped brow, long white whiskers and luminous blue eyes set in slanted lids, which give me an oriental appearance.

I know precisely how to exploit my feline mystique, so no one really knows what lies behind my inscrutable stare. My manner is sometimes interpreted as being a little haughty and condescending but, in reality, I am very affectionate and loyal to people I like. Some would say that I am pampered by Pam and Graham but the truth is that our lives have become so interwoven during the sixteen years we have been together that they treat me as one of the family—indeed there are times when I feel more human than feline. In some respects, there has been a reversal of roles in our house so that now I am the one who worries when they stay out late, unable to settle for the night until they are home—unlike a few years ago when they waited anxiously for my call to be let in, after I returned from a nocturnal outing.

I had just settled myself on the lounger when Pam appeared in the doorway of the dining room, which opens on to the terrace.

'Ah there you are, Tia! I won't be long—I'll just get some tea and then we can have a snooze together.'

How lovely! I turned and smiled as I stretched full length and rolled over to create a space for her. It would be pleasant to relax with Pam because, when Graham is around, I usually devote my attention to him. I knew she would need some time to unwind after the hurried preparations for Graham's journey, but hoped she would play a record when she had rested so that we could dance together. I could almost hear the music of *La Cumparsita*

pom pom pom pom    pompompom   pom pom pom pom pom pom

and pictured us tangoing cheek to cheek—my right paw in her left hand and my left arm wound round her neck, as she supported my weight by holding me firmly against her chest. I imagined us twirling and swaying in time to the music, my ecstatic purrs resonating in my throat, until we ended with a couple of whirls before collapsing into a chair when the music stopped.

While I luxuriated on the deep cushion enjoying the warmth of Mallorca, I wondered whether Graham was bringing me back a new hooded basket—mine had become somewhat dilapidated, due to my habit of sharpening my claws on the cane every morning—but the tone of his voice had implied something rather more significant.

A sense of well-being overcame me and I drifted into a reverie as I relaxed in the tranquillity of the mountains, almost oblivious to the incessant chirping of the cicadas. As I lay there, I contrasted my lifestyle with the time before I was adopted by Pam and Graham; recalling the dreadful sameness of those early years when I lived in a small house in Surrey with a middle-aged woman, her two rumbustious children and a somewhat antagonistic old female Siamese. The aged cat had regarded me as a rival for the affection of her owner, but her jealousy was unjustified because I had been acquired for breeding purposes and not as a pet.

My monotonous existence was only relieved by an occasional day at a cat show where I competed against other Siamese, eventually achieving championship status. At these events, I was able to converse with friendly cats in adjacent cages, which made the day more interesting; although once, as I was being put into my pen, I smiled at a female chocolate-point alongside who responded by swearing at me and then continued to growl for some time. Her hostility astounded me but I realised that it sprang from her recognition of unbeatable competition, when I saw that there were no rosettes pinned to her cage after the judging.

My owner dressed smartly for the shows and looked quite elegant, but one woman always wore an extraordinary hat crowned with a cluster of pheasants' feathers. She had an unfortunate habit of thrusting her face against our cages to scrutinise us—many a poor unsuspecting cat taking a short nap was rudely awakened by the prod of a feather penetrating the wire. My owner always stationed herself in front of my cage to protect me from any injury, because a poke in the eye, even from a feather, could destroy the chance of a championship. The hideous hat could be seen from a considerable distance, its feathers waving as the woman walked towards us, so we were able to warn one another of her approach. We all laughed when one enterprising queen seized the opportunity to grab the feathers as they entered her cage and, quick as a flash, severed them from the hat with her teeth. By the time the woman realised what was happening, the loathsome hat, minus its feathers, lay on the ground in the dust and that was the last we saw of it.

To relieve the tedium of my life at the house, I spent many hours plotting how to escape and waited patiently for a suitable moment. My chance came unexpectedly one morning when my owner, thinking I was asleep, left the back door ajar while she went to find some money to pay the milkman. I leaped from my basket, darted out between his legs and raced headlong through the gate into the street.

It was only when I was free that I realised I had never considered my next move. Which way should I run? I had no idea what to do—my name was already being called, so I had to act quickly because my flight had been discovered.

'Quick, hide over here gal!' exclaimed a friendly feline voice.

'Where are you? I can't see you.'

'Over here under the laurel hedge—hurry now before they spot you.'

A scruffy female tortoiseshell, with a large nick out of her left ear, was crouched at the base of the hedge—almost hidden by the lower branches. I quickly tucked myself beside her, out of sight of any pursuers.

'Thank you very much, that was kind of you; I was getting a trifle apprehensive.'

'Don't you talk posh! You certainly are one elegant lady and I've never seen a coat like yours. What's your name and why are you on the run?'

'My name is Tia Maria and I'm Siamese. Normally I'm shut in all day and only go out on a lead, but I've managed to escape.'

'I'm not surprised you wanted to be free but you're fortunate to have a home. My name's Mitzi and I have to fend for myself, but I get by. I know all the best eating-places around here; if you fancy a meal, follow me and we'll go to the back of Joe's fish and chip shop—he likes cats and he's always a pushover if you look hungry enough. You won't have a problem—they must keep you on a starvation diet!' she exclaimed, eyeing my sleek figure.

'I'm not very keen on fish.'

'Get you! I think myself lucky if I find some scraps at the bottom of an old sardine tin, but if you prefer meat we can try the Paradise Café—they do steak and chips and we can have a look in their garbage!'

The thought of rummaging through someone's rubbish bins struck me as revolting, but I was anxious not to offend her and reluctantly agreed to accompany her to avoid being left alone.

'How long have you been on your own?' I asked as we strolled side-by-side, wending our way towards the café.

'Oh! For some time now. The girl I lived with fell in love with a young man and they got married. Unfortunately, he became quite ill whenever I was in the room and they discovered that he was allergic to cats. For the sake of her husband, she found me another home but within a week I realised the people didn't really want me, so I took to the streets and was soon picked up by a good-looking tom. I thought my luck had changed but he turned out to be a bully and treated me very badly; I left him after he bit off half my ear and I soon learned how to look after myself—it's not so bad living rough if you know the ropes.'

'I've been shut in since I was a kitten and the only other cat in the house resents my being there,' I replied.

'You'll find the perfect mate one day, they're not all like the ones I fall for,' said my shabby friend.

She knew all the short cuts and led me in a complex path through gardens and over fences. Where the trellis on top was blocked, because roses and other shrubs had gained a stranglehold, we used hollows scuffed out by other animals to squeeze ourselves underneath.

At the end of the gardens, we crossed a street and found ourselves in a gloomy alley. Piles of filthy rubbish were scattered everywhere and weeds filled the cracks in the broken paving of the dismal pathway. Fear overcame me when I looked up and saw high concrete fences covered with slimy green lichen—making them impossible to scale. I became desperate to get out of the sinister place and increased my pace, forcing Mitzi to do the same until we burst out into a wide road and headed towards a smart parade of shops. A track at the side led to a rutted yard serving the rear entrances; it was dotted with potholes containing murky water and the litter-strewn area contrasted sharply with the stylish appearance of the frontages. My guide walked purposefully towards some foul-smelling bins lined against a crumbling brick wall and selected one which was overflowing with the remains of several hundred meals.

I was both flattered and revolted when Mitzi returned, carrying an almost naked bone that she deposited at my feet with the pride of a chef presenting a *médaillon de boeuf*. Ugh, how could she! Instinctively I began to wash

# Mitzi

myself furiously in the hope that the dreadful smell would not adhere to my fur.

'Thank you, but I'm still not hungry. You have it—you must be starving.'

Even though I was beginning to feel a few pangs of hunger, there was no way that I could have touched it—let alone eat it! I sat a little distance away, watching disgustedly as she gnawed the few remaining scraps from the bone with obvious enjoyment and then went back for another. It was heartbreaking for me to see someone who had known a comfortable life forced to scavenge to exist—even though she made light of her misfortune.

The day was bitterly cold, and my fur was already becoming damp from intermittent drops of rain that threatened to turn to a steady downpour at any moment. As I sat in the middle of the dirty yard, I realised that I could never adapt to such a primitive existence. What I had imagined would be an exciting experience had turned into an awareness of life in the raw and I started to tremble with fear. What should I do next? Inevitably, there would come a time when I would have to eat or drink something in order to survive.

My name was again being called and, as the sound came nearer, I realised that I would have to surrender and return to my dull but hygienic lifestyle. I called to my friend who was still enjoying her meal:

'Mitzi, my owner is getting frantic—I must go to her. It's been nice meeting you but I'll have to leave you now.'

Mitzi, who was endeavouring to strip the last traces of meat from her latest bone, was so absorbed in her feast that she could only spare enough time to give me a brief nod of farewell. I trotted off in the direction of the voice and soon came face to face with my owner.

'Tia, where have you been and what have you been doing?' she said, picking me up. 'You are a naughty cat to give me so much worry; half the neighbourhood is searching for you and I must let everyone know that you are safe.'

I was happy to see her and could sense that she was relieved to have found me relatively quickly. I rested in her arms as she carried me back to the house and the warmth of her body was soon transmitted to mine. Thereafter escape was no longer uppermost in my thoughts and I resigned myself to my dull life—although sometimes I wondered how my tattered friend was faring and admired her ability to make the most of her harsh existence.

# 2. Ben

My owner decided that it was high time for me to be introduced to a male with a suitable pedigree, before I escaped again and selected my own mate from the local rabble. The prospect of a handsome beau was very appealing, if only as a break from my usual routine, and I listened eagerly as arrangements were made for me to be taken to a cattery some miles away.

On the appointed day, after I had been groomed from head to tail, we drove several miles to the cattery and waited for what seemed an eternity. My owner placed my basket on the floor near her feet and I amused myself by extending my claws and stretching a paw through the wire door—watching in fascination as long ladders spread up her new stockings. To my surprise, she allowed me to continue my game without a word of reprimand—possibly because she did not wish to be seen chastising such an innocent-looking cat! Just when I was becoming bored, a white-coated member of the staff came to collect me and, as I was carried away, I saw my owner departing with as much dignity as she could muster with her stockings in tatters.

My accommodation consisted of a wire pen with a concrete run and a small wooden hut—a pile of straw in a corner of the sleeping quarters being the only concession to comfort. Left on my own and feeling lonely, humiliated and extremely nervous, I calmed myself by energetically licking my front paws and biting my claws. As a diversion, I snuffed every corner of my temporary abode and then turned my attention to a larger shed alongside with a pen that appeared to be empty.

Suddenly, a male seal-point Siamese emerged through the cat-flap of the neighbouring shed. He paused to look at me through the wire netting separating us and, in an instant, all my fears evaporated. Large and muscular with a fine dark head, bright blue eyes and almost black ears—he was so stunning that I was completely overwhelmed. The glossy brown fur on his back shaded to cream on his chest, flanks and stomach, while his legs and tail matched the black of his ears and mask. As our eyes met, I fell desperately in love with him and knew that I had met the partner of my dreams.

He strolled over without speaking and scrutinised me from the tip of my nose to the end of my tail—so obviously sophisticated, and possibly even a little arrogant, that he made me feel shy and confused.

'Hello,' he said, 'my name's Ben—what's yours?'

Although my mouth was dry, I just managed to stammer: 'Tia Maria.'

'It suits you, I was admiring your lissom figure and exquisite colouring,' he said, switching on the charm.

'You're a chocolate-point aren't you—will you be staying the night?'

Somewhat taken aback by such a direct approach, I glanced towards my travelling basket that was dangling from a large hook on the other side of my pen.

'It would seem so,' I answered, very much on my dignity.

'You look even more beautiful when you are riled!' he exclaimed. 'With your exceptional markings and my championship status at the shows, our kittens should be unbeatable.' Then he abruptly turned away and walked back into his cabin, leaving me wondering what to do next.

Would a couple of my loudest banshee howls produce some action? I took a deep breath and created a deafening noise. Staff came running from all directions to discover the cause of the commotion. One of the helpers stroked me to calm me down, but I was left alone again when it was apparent that nothing was wrong and, before long, Ben re-emerged from his house.

'I was trying to have a nap. What on earth possessed you to make a din like that?'

'I was feeling miserable and lonely,' I replied.

'There's nothing to be upset about; I expect you're tired after your journey. Try to get some rest and after dinner we'll be together and can talk some more.'

He really was incredibly handsome and *so* charming! I decided to take his advice and, adopting my slinkiest walk, made my way into the little wooden house at the end of my pen, where I slept until I was awakened by the sound of voices. A pretty young girl with dark brown hair and twinkling eyes appeared in the doorway; she was carrying a meal of chicken in jelly and spoke softly to me as she placed the food on the floor. I had not realised how hungry I was and abandoned my normal genteel eating habits to greedily gobble up every scrap.

A little while later, a communicating door between our two sheds was opened and Ben put his head through the aperture.

'Ah, there you are!' he said. 'Come on in.'

I had barely entered his quarters when the door behind me was slammed shut. Prowling around Ben's cabin, I noted that, although it was larger than mine, it was equally austere—apart from a small mat on the linoleum-covered floor and a high shelf running across one end.

We sat down together while Ben told me about his life. He only left his pen to compete in cat shows and was largely dependent on visiting queens for news of the world outside. This made me conscious of an empathy with him because, like me, he was a prisoner of circumstance. His superb build and excellent pedigree made him far too valuable to be allowed any freedom.

He kissed me as we talked and I in turn nuzzled him shyly.

'You have a fascinating little beard under your chin,' he said.

'Oh is that what it is—I haven't seen it myself although I can feel it when I wash my face!' I exclaimed.

'Yes, they're not very common, but yours certainly becomes you.'

By then, I was completely relaxed because I am very susceptible to flattery. Some time later, I drifted off to sleep, my head resting on his flank, and it was early the next morning before I awoke with a start as the large door to the pen was opened and the owner of the cattery walked in.

'Just look at them!' She exclaimed to the pretty girl who had fed me the previous evening. 'They obviously got on well together because Ben is usually alone on his shelf in the morning. Go and get her things because she'll be collected shortly.'

## Ben

I had not realised that I would be leaving Ben so soon and we were only able to manage a hurried farewell before I was picked up and secured in my basket.

'I love you Ben,' I cried. 'I'll never forget you.'

'I love you too—I'll remember you always.'

We parted with sadness in our hearts, knowing that it was beyond our capability to organise another meeting— the only glimmer of hope was that my owner might arrange for me to visit Ben again, if our kittens turned out to be champions.

Ben was constantly in my thoughts and it was not long before I knew that I was expecting his kittens. For the first time in my life, I was aware of an inner serenity and the days flew by as I eagerly awaited their arrival. However, this feeling of tranquillity was short-lived because, just before they were due, I became ill and the vet had to be summoned. By the time he arrived, I had produced two stillborn kittens and, after examining me, he turned to my anxious owner and told her that an immediate operation was essential to save the others.

I remember nothing more about that day and was delirious for nearly a week. When I recovered, I was overjoyed to learn that two kittens had survived—but my secret hopes of meeting my lover again were dashed when I overheard the vet remark to my owner:

'She's such a beautiful cat; it's a great pity that she can't have any more kittens—but she only just pulled through this time and it would be madness to risk her having another litter.'

I was desolate and lay in my basket anguishing at the thought of never seeing Ben again; my only comfort being the knowledge that at least I had two of his offspring that were as beautiful as he had predicted. The male was registered as Caligula, but was immediately nicknamed Ziggy; the female was registered as Cleopatra, but she never acquired a nickname because she went to another home at the age of six weeks.

Ziggy grew quickly and, as his markings developed, it became apparent that he would be a seal-point like his father. He started to resemble Ben more every day and I watched his progress with pride, tinged with sadness as I continued to yearn for my lost love.

Our owner was very attached to the cantankerous female Siamese who had been with her for many years. The geriatric cat accompanied her everywhere, while Ziggy and I were left alone in the house to amuse ourselves as best we could. Ziggy had a mischievous streak and was frequently punished for the damage he caused by climbing the curtains or jumping on to the furniture—occasionally leaving broken ornaments strewn across the floor. He began to associate human beings with chastisement and eventually became so nervous when people were present that he would slink around with his belly touching the floor.

I too underwent a change in temperament and dedicated myself to the responsibilities of motherhood. I constantly worried about Ziggy and finally reached the conclusion that he needed more space in which to work off some of his surplus energy—although I had no idea how this could be achieved.

# 3. Ziggy

My operation negated our owner's plans to breed Siamese and she abandoned the project—opting to move from her house to a flat, which was far too small to accommodate two children and three cats. Since the bad-tempered female was too old to be parted from her, Ziggy and I were the ones who would have to go. While she made arrangements for our future, she housed us temporarily in a boutique, which she owned in the centre of a large town; it was there that fate stepped in and changed our lives.

The boutique was fairly large and extended over two fully carpeted floors. It smelled of expensive perfume and new clothes with an underlying hint of perspiration and old shoes. Most humans seemed unaware of the odour but it nauseated me because of my acute sense of smell. Fortunately, our basket had been placed in a corner of the upper floor, well away from the changing rooms, and it was there that we spent most of our time. If anyone approached us, Ziggy would run off and hide because he hated the well-meant attention of customers who wanted to stroke him. His behaviour became increasingly neurotic and, several times a day, I had to calm him by licking his head until he responded by nuzzling me and telling me how much he loved me.

We were sitting in our basket, wondering what was going to happen to us, when a tall, slim, smartly dressed woman examining dresses on a nearby rail, turned and noticed us.

'What lovely Siamese!' she exclaimed.

'Yes, they are mother and son,' replied our owner. 'Unfortunately, I can't keep them here much longer so I'm trying to find a good home for them.'

The woman nodded understandingly. 'My name is Rita, by the way; I would love to have them myself but I'm afraid it wouldn't be practical. However, I have a friend who has owned Siamese cats all her life and she was very upset when her last one died recently at the age of fourteen. Would you like me to contact her and see if she's interested?' asked Rita.

Our owner responded enthusiastically: 'By all means, I have an advertisement appearing in the local paper this week-end but that still gives your friend a day or two to decide—naturally, I must be satisfied that there is sufficient room for them and that they would be well treated.'

'That won't be a problem,' said Rita. 'Pam and her husband live in a country house set in three acres of grounds and they both absolutely adore Siamese.'

That afternoon, Rita's friend telephoned and arranged to come and see us the following morning. I had an overwhelming feeling of relief at the prospect of leaving the boutique because I had become very anxious for Ziggy's safety. The shop door opened straight on to the main street of the town and, knowing how impetuous he could be, I feared that one day he would dash out and run into the busy road. Apart from that, it was tedious being cooped up all day and a new home out in the country, well away from the hazards of the town, sounded perfect.

The next morning a petite woman with short blond hair and a friendly smile appeared at the top of the stairs. She looked around and started to walk towards the corner where we sat posing in our basket. Ziggy immediately sprang out and ran towards her as she got down on her knees to greet him. She laughed and smiled as he tried to push his head into her lap—the two of them oblivious to the stares of several amused customers. I watched in amazement because Ziggy was displaying exceptional affection and encouraging her to respond. Our owner was also astonished by his uncharacteristic behaviour.

'I've never seen him act like that before!' she exclaimed, as Ziggy continued to nuzzle his new friend—purring even louder.

'I telephoned yesterday,' said Pam as she tried to get to her feet, which proved rather difficult because Ziggy refused to budge from her lap and clung tightly to her.

'I assumed it must be you,' replied our owner. 'Rita said that you were a lover of Siamese and you obviously have an affinity with them.'

Although I was relieved to see that Ziggy had instantly accepted Pam, despite his nervousness, I wanted it clearly understood that we were together—so I moved forward with a smile on my face to ensure that I was not overlooked. I need not have worried because, as I approached, she reached out and expertly stroked the length of my body, ending with a gentle tug on my tail. Thereafter, Ziggy and I listened intently to what was being discussed.

'Rita told me they were beautiful cats, but they really are quite exceptional—and so different! What are their names?'

'The chocolate-point is Tia Maria; the seal-point is her son and we call him Ziggy. They both have good pedigrees but they can't be used for breeding. If you would like to have them, they're yours—I'm sure you'll give them a good home. I had been anticipating a possible problem because Ziggy has a nervous disposition, but he seems to have taken to you already.'

'I should love to have them and you can rest assured that we'll treat them as part of the family—if you can bring them to my house this afternoon you'll be able to see where they will live.'

Our owner agreed and a few hours later she drove us about twelve miles out of the town. I usually hate car rides because they frequently end at the vet but, on this occasion, I sat on the parcel shelf eagerly taking in every detail of the passing scene. It was not long before we turned into a gateway and continued up a winding drive bordered by wide lawns, impressive flowerbeds and numerous mature trees.

'Mum, what lovely trees to climb,' Ziggy enthused, eyeing them like a boy selecting sweets in a tuck-shop.

'Yes, but behave yourself today and stick close to me,' I said warningly.

As we arrived at the house, I felt my body tingle with excitement at the prospect of our new lifestyle. Pam came out to meet us and, after greeting our owner, turned to us saying:

'Welcome to your new home both of you.'

Her husband, who was tall with dark hair framing a kind face, joined her.

'Graham, let me introduce you to Tia Maria and her son Ziggy who have come to live with us.'

'Aren't you beautiful!' he exclaimed as he gently lifted me out of the car, burying his face in the soft fur of my neck and giving me a kiss. 'Where did you find them, Pam?'

'Let's go inside and I'll tell you the whole story,' she replied as she reached into the car for Ziggy, who was sitting with a stupid grin on his face—he immediately jumped into her arms and snuggled happily against her. We were carried through a hallway into a large sitting room and placed on a white hearthrug, the remainder of the floor being covered with thick carpet. Comfortable chairs and sofas, laden with cushions, were arranged in a semi-circle around the fireplace, creating a formal yet cosy atmosphere. The other furniture was polished to a mirror finish and several delicate porcelain figurines were precariously arranged on low tables—I made a mental note to caution Ziggy that he must contain his natural exuberance in these surroundings.

Pam served the tea and related to her husband the events leading up to our meeting in the boutique, while we settled happily on the hearthrug listening to what she was saying and minutely observing every detail of the room. When Pam had finished, our owner rose to leave—explaining that she had to return to her shop but was confident that she was leaving us in good hands. I had been with her for nearly three years and felt a lump rise in my throat as she departed, but I quickly recovered when I saw how completely relaxed and contented Ziggy had become. He was my main concern and I was astounded at the speed with which he was adapting to his new environment.

We were confined to the house until we got our bearings—otherwise we were unrestricted and free to explore every room. Making the most of this opportunity, we jumped on to the windowsills to look out at the sweeping green lawns, surrounded by colourful herbaceous borders and well-manicured yew hedges, before racing upstairs to explore the bedrooms—it was already obvious that life was going to be extremely pleasant in our new home.

We learned that there were two grown-up daughters in the family; Claire, who had a flat in London, and her younger sister Laura, who was still living at home. We met Laura that evening and it was evident from her delight at seeing us that she, too, loved Siamese. She made a tremendous fuss of us and we responded by purring loudly while nudging her with our heads and twining our bodies around her legs. She was completely fascinated by Ziggy's breathtaking appearance and, from that moment on, they had a special rapport.

During that first day, I was a trifle emotional and anxious to ensure that nothing should disrupt the happy atmosphere. In consequence, I rather overplayed the part of the heavy mother—stationing myself under the dining room table and giving vent to my pent-up feelings by swearing at Ziggy and issuing an endless stream of instructions:

'Don't scratch the carpet, don't climb the curtains and don't claw the chairs!' I was turning into a real nag-bag and he was more than a little surprised by my constant carping.

'What's the matter with you, Mum?' he asked. 'I really am trying to be good.'

'Yes, I know,' I replied. 'But we must be particularly careful not to offend the family because this is a lovely home and I can't bear the thought of living anywhere else. Just be patient until we are allowed outside, then you can climb trees and run about as much as you wish.'

That evening, two new collars and leads were produced and we were taken into the grounds to have some exercise. This did not worry me as I had been trained to walk correctly on a lead but, unfortunately, Ziggy had not.

'Try and keep calm and just walk normally,' I told him. However, he ignored my instructions and became hysterical, thrashing about like a fish on the end of a line, leaping high into the air and doing double somersaults until, finally, he slipped his collar and sped off towards a fence at the bottom of the garden with Graham in hot pursuit. They were an extraordinary sight—Ziggy, racing across the lawn with his ears pinned back and his tail stiff as a rudder stretched out behind him, and Graham following with his tall body bent almost double as he attempted to grab Ziggy's tail.

Pam carried me back to the house, where I jumped on to a windowsill overlooking the lawn, and I watched with consternation as Ziggy scaled a high wooden fence separating the grounds from the next property. My mind was in turmoil, Graham should have known that you never chase Siamese—it only makes them nervous. I was transfixed with horror when Ziggy turned and attacked Graham viciously, scratching his arm and biting deeply into the flesh between the first finger and thumb of his right hand as he stretched up to seize him.

Now he's really blown it, I thought, why in the world did he have to do a thing like that! I had never known Ziggy bite anyone before and it was a tragedy that he had done this just when everything had been going so smoothly.

Even though in considerable pain, Graham did not release his hold on Ziggy. Clutching the scruff of his neck with his damaged hand, he used the other to grab first his tail and then a hind leg and drag him off the fence. Still grasping him firmly, he brought him back to the house and then collapsed onto the sofa holding a handkerchief to his hand, which was bleeding profusely from several deep scratches and the bite—his face was as white as a sheet.

I cowered in a corner watching apprehensively while Ziggy made a dash for the stairs. I knew that he would take refuge under one of the beds and decided not to disturb him until he had calmed down—so I kept quiet and waited to see what would happen next.

As Pam applied disinfectant and Laura handed him a large brandy, Graham stated emphatically:

'Ziggy will have to go—we can't have a cat that behaves like a wild animal.'

Mother and daughter began to cry.

'Please give him another chance,' they chorused. 'Ziggy was obviously absolutely terrified.'

Then followed a lengthy debate and I listened anxiously for the outcome. What would I do if Ziggy were banished? I loved him, not only because he was my son but also he was my last link with Ben. My ears swivelled round and started to twitch as I strained to hear what each of them had to say. Initially, Graham was adamant that Ziggy must go but, in response to their pleas—although he was not entirely convinced, he reluctantly agreed that Ziggy would be forgiven this once and allowed to stay—providing he settled down quickly. I breathed a sigh of relief that Ziggy and I had been spared separation; it was a beautiful house and the grounds were spectacular but life there would have been empty without my son.

After this highly emotional experience, everyone retired to bed. However, a couple of hours later, I was aroused by the sound of Pam and Graham coming downstairs and getting the car out of the garage. I lay awake wondering where they had gone in the middle of the night and it was dawn before I heard wheels crunching up the drive as they returned. Exhausted by the trauma of the previous evening, Ziggy slept soundly throughout—unaware that he was on probation.

At breakfast the next morning, we overheard Pam telling Laura what had happened during the night. Graham's hand had become so swollen and painful that they had gone to the casualty department of the local hospital, where he was given an anti-tetanus injection and instructed to keep the arm upright for several hours.

It was more than a week before Graham's hand returned to its normal size and I spent most of that time with him in his study, sitting on the papers he was reading or walking over his computer keyboard introducing extraneous characters. Together we invented a game involving my clinging to the seat of his swivel chair, while he rotated me like a top. Another game we both enjoyed was bumper cars, during which he would push the chair at great speed and swing it sideways at the last moment to avoid a collision with the other furniture. I am sure Pam must have wondered what all the noise was about because Graham made whirring sounds while we played, but she was very discreet and did not make any comment about her husband's juvenile pursuits.

# 4. Incidents in the Garden

It took a long time for Graham to forgive Ziggy and he was not wholly at ease with him for several months. In the evenings, when the family sat watching television, I would sit on Graham's lap, while Ziggy would drape himself over Pam or lie on his back on the sofa in a completely abandoned state, gazing lovingly into her eyes. He rarely left her side and followed her everywhere—even sitting on the carpet outside the bathroom door, with his front paws tucked out of sight, while she took a bath.

When he was not with Pam, Ziggy would often visit Laura as she studied at a small desk in her bedroom. He could not resist springing up and settling himself on top of her notebook as she wrote—his head swivelling round and round as he watched the movement of her pencil, which fascinated him so much that he would try to catch it and bite the top. He would have continued the game indefinitely had Laura allowed it, but she found it impossible to concentrate with a large Siamese pawing at her pencil. In desperation, she would pick him up and shut him outside her bedroom door where he would sit and yowl—informing everyone that he had been very badly treated.

When we were given the freedom of the garden, Ziggy was able to race about the lawns and climb the trees to his heart's content. I had never seen him so happy and was constantly thankful to our new family for adopting us. A cat-flap was installed, which was normally left open during the day but locked at night and whenever the whole family went out. Every morning we would scramble through it and inspect the grounds while breakfast was being prepared. I will never forget the many sights and smells; the heady honeysuckle scent of the great banks of azaleas in springtime, the subtler fragrance of the roses on summer mornings and the dew, glistening like tiny pearls, decorating the hundreds of intricate webs on the shrubs in autumn.

One day, after Graham had left the house early to go to London, we were patrolling the garden while the air was still slightly moist, to make sure that everything was in order. On reaching the herbaceous border, Ziggy suddenly leaped into the air and dropped on to a mouse, which had been careless enough to remain sitting there as he approached. He was immensely proud and gently carried it back to the house to show Pam how clever he was. I followed him through the cat-flap and watched as he dropped it at her feet, gazing up at her expecting to be congratulated. We were both thrilled by his achievement and thought that she would be equally delighted but, much to our surprise, she was obviously very annoyed. Meanwhile the mouse seized the opportunity to scuttle under a bookcase.

'Ziggy, get that filthy thing out of here at once! What on earth did you think you were doing bringing it into the house?' she exclaimed.

What was the matter with her? It was a perfectly good mouse—not even dead! We watched in amazement as she ran from the room, returning a few moments later with a large butterfly net in her hand. We soon deduced what she had in mind and, while she waited by the bookcase with the net poised, we ran round to the other side and chased the mouse out. She brought the net down quickly but just missed and the mouse managed to escape to safety under an armchair. We obligingly went round behind the chair, baring our teeth and emitting snarls that would have terrified an elephant—let alone a small mouse. This sequence was repeated several times with Ziggy getting increasingly excited.

Although Ziggy enjoyed being the centre of Pam's attention, he tended to have a grasshopper mind and became bored very easily. Tiring of this repetitive game, he extended one of his long arms, hooked the mouse out from its hiding place, grabbed it by the neck and carried it through the cat-flap—which, of course, was what Pam had wanted all along.

I enjoyed our morning strolls across the dew-soaked lawns that were Graham's pride and joy, but once, as I was returning along the front of the house, I felt the earth move under my feet. What was that? I stopped dead in my tracks to listen and, as I did so, I felt something pushing at my underbelly, causing me to leap into the air with all four legs extended. I turned to see what had nudged me and saw a fresh mound of rich brown earth in a neat pile—it moved as I watched and more earth cascaded down from the centre. Ziggy had wandered off to the herbaceous border and was unaware of what was happening, so I called to him:

'Ziggy, come and look at this!'

'What's up, Mum?' he asked, as he sauntered towards me.

'A small heap of earth has suddenly appeared in Graham's lawn and I can't think what it can be—it's just over there,' I said.

As we looked, another mound appeared about a yard from the first—this was too much for Ziggy who dashed towards the nearest one and started digging frantically with his front paws.

'Be careful, Ziggy, let's tell Graham before his whole lawn is ruined by all these bumps—look there's another one!' I cried.

Even as we watched, another previously well-manicured part of the lawn suddenly heaved and a trickle of earth appeared. We headed back to the house to get Graham, crashed in through the cat-flap, and found Pam busy preparing breakfast, but there was no sign of Graham— surely he had not gone back to bed. We were about to mount the stairs to search for him when we heard him come into the house.

'Nothing much in the post this morning. What's the matter with the cats? As I was returning from the letterbox, I saw them streaking home as if the devil were after them!'

At the sound of his voice, we turned and both of us emitted several banshees as we walked towards the front door, urging him to follow.

'I'd better see what's the matter,' he said to Pam. 'Shan't be long and then we can all have breakfast.'

He opened the front door and we rushed towards the scene of the crime, pausing to allow him to catch up with us, and waiting for the tirade that we knew would follow.

'It's a blasted mole,' he stormed. 'My beautiful lawn is absolutely ruined—I'll get him!'

We both felt sorry for him and tried to console him by sitting a short distance away miaowing soulfully.

Graham dashed to the tool shed and returned carrying a plastic bucket and a spade, which he plunged deeply into the new molehill. Levering the handle sharply downwards, he caused a cascade of fine earth to shoot high into the air together with a very startled mole. His intention was to quickly drop the spade, grab the bucket and catch the mole in mid-air, but he overbalanced and sprawled full length on the lawn. Ziggy, who had been watching all this with great interest, could not believe his eyes when he saw the mole spreadeagled on the ground less than a yard in front of him. He quickly pounced on it, seized it between his teeth and ran off growling—defying anyone to follow him.

There was no sign of any more tunnelling, so Graham picked himself up, flattened the mounds with the spade, and we returned to the house for breakfast.

'What did they want?' asked Pam as soon as we appeared. 'Where's Ziggy?'

'He's gone off with a mole! I'm afraid we now have them in the front lawn. Only the other day the gardener over the road told me that he was having trouble with them and had experimented with smoke bombs, burying grapefruit skins in the tunnels, and setting various types of trap—all to no avail. However, he claimed that an infallible method is to shove a spade into the centre of a new mound and shoot the earth upwards, bringing the mole with it, and then catch it in a bucket. That's what I was trying to do, but he didn't warn me that it needs practice to let go of a spade and pick up a bucket quickly without falling over, and before the mole is grabbed by a large Siamese.'

Every morning, we strolled round the perimeter of the grounds returning when the smell of freshly made toast and coffee signalled that breakfast was ready. We knew that ours would be waiting for us on the floor near the table and, since Ziggy was a male, I observed feline protocol and waited while he ate his fill before I approached the plate.

As his mother, I expected him to reciprocate by treating me with the respect that was my due and I reacted sharply one morning when he was cheeky. He was exploring the flat roof of the garden shed where the lawnmower was kept and I spotted him preparing to spring down, instead of using the pine tree by which he had ascended.

'Don't jump, come down the tree!' I shouted.

This had no effect and he still made as if to jump.

'Didn't you hear me?' I remonstrated.

'I'm all right, I can do it—it's not that high.'

Having no alternative, I scaled the tree and sprang onto the roof.

'You're to climb down at once,' I said as I walked threateningly towards him.

'Shan't.'

On hearing this, I attempted to box his ears to teach him a lesson—but he was too quick for me and, as I walked away, he tried to bite my bottom. This was too much and I turned and growled at him, extending my claws as a stern warning that any repeat of such insolence would not be tolerated.

It was not always easy being a single parent, but most of the time we were totally in accord and enjoyed our life together—although Ziggy was quick to exploit any lapses on my part.

One occasion was when I lost my collar. Ziggy had overcome the neurosis that had caused friction between him and Graham and now wore his collar proudly—because he considered that its colour matched his exceptional blue eyes; mine was fluorescent green—not that my eyes are green but it complemented my chocolate and cream colouring. I loved wearing it but, unfortunately, it got caught on the branch of a tree when I was out hunting. As it was elasticised, I managed to struggle free and tried to sneak into the house without Pam seeing me but she heard me as I came in through the cat-flap.

Tia, are you all right? What's happened—your collar is missing.'

At that moment, Ziggy shot through the cat-flap and he too saw my naked neck.

'Mum, where's your collar?' he said, carefully flaunting his own to show that he was not careless enough to lose it.

'I was after a bird and my collar became entangled in the branch of a tree; I managed to pull myself free but had to leave it behind as I descended,' I explained.

'Then you know where it is!' he cried, getting quite excited. 'Why don't we go and fetch it?'

'Not now, it's firmly attached and we couldn't release it. In any case, I'm exhausted after struggling to free myself and I don't want to leave the warmth of the house.'

Periodically, I passed the tree where my collar dangled tantalisingly from the branch, although it was still securely lodged. However, some weeks later, when strolling in the winter sunshine, I was surprised to see it lying on a flower bed—a strong wind must have blown it down and it had travelled some distance before falling to the ground. I was delighted and proudly carried it back to the house in my mouth. Pushing through the cat-flap, I approached the family who were having tea together and triumphantly dropped it at their feet.

'Look what Tia's found!' Graham exclaimed, leaning down to stroke me. 'What a clever girl!'

'Yes, I never thought we'd see that again; it's amazing that she was intelligent enough to carry it back,' added Pam.

I sat soaking up their compliments, lowering my eyelids demurely while purring sweetly. Ziggy, who had been lying nonchalantly on his back amongst the cushions inviting admiration, became jealous of my taking centre stage and sauntered off to recover his equanimity.

# 5. Felicity

Pam's car was a dark brown Austin 3-litre, which the family had affectionately nicknamed Felicity, although that model was usually referred to less kindly in the motor trade as 'the squint-eyed pig'.

Felicity normally went like the wind, especially in response to a kick-down on her accelerator pedal, but even when new she broke into a sweat and overheated at the slightest sign of traffic—stalling at every red light. Pam was usually a nervous wreck by the time we finally managed to get through a congested town, but once back on the open road Felicity would quickly cool down and behave properly. Ziggy and I loved the car because it had a very wide and comfortable rear seat with a central arm rest, which provided each of us with a separate compartment cushioned on three sides.

On one occasion, Pam drove us to the vet for a routine visit and, on the return journey up the hill, Felicity appeared to be very sluggish. In spite of energetic encouragement from Pam, she would hardly go above a walking pace. When we eventually reached the house, Graham came out to greet us.

'Well, how were they? Did they behave themselves with the vet and not try to bite him?'

What else! I thought. Ziggy might have bitten Graham once when he was terrified, but we were not in the habit of biting people and anyway the vet had the upper hand—holding a syringe!

'Yes, they were marvellous! They sat and looked at him with their big blue eyes and completely bowled him over. However, I'm worried about Felicity; she seems to have lost all her power, it was quite exhausting coaxing her back today.'

'I'll have a look at her when we've had tea; I expect you could do with a cup and I'm sure the cats are waiting for their milk.'

Later that afternoon, Graham went out to where Felicity was parked in front of the garage. He opened her bonnet and examined everything in sight. Ziggy and I sat watching him as his fingers probed all her private parts that we had not seen before. He removed several items, placed them on the lawn beside the drive and, after inspecting them, returned them to their allotted places.

As I moved nearer to encourage him in his search for the cause of the problem, I sensed that another animal had been inside the bonnet. What was that scent? It was familiar yet I could not quite identify it. The engine was still warm from the journey and the smell of hot oil disguised the aroma, but I was able to detect that it was strongest near a large pipe low down at the front of the car.

By this time, Graham had removed Felicity's huge air filter and started to dismantle it on the drive. He gasped as he opened it and saw that the interior was tightly packed with uniform cubes of bread; this so bewildered him that he called Pam to come and see what he had found.

Ziggy and I went nearer to inspect the object that Graham had deposited on the drive. Now that it had been removed from the car, the smell of hot oil was not so overwhelming and I knew immediately what animal had stuffed the bread inside. Most cats have quicksilver minds, unlike humans who can sometimes be rather slow and ponderous. I wondered how long it would take Pam and Graham to identify the scent and waited expectantly for Pam to respond to Graham's call.

She came out of the house almost immediately.

'Gracious!' cried Pam, as she inspected the air filter. 'That's the bread I put out for the birds. How did it get there?'

'I've no idea,' said Graham, 'but I don't think it could have been a bird, perhaps a mouse or a rat. How long have you been putting the bread out?'

'Oh, for quite some time, I thought the birds were enjoying it because it disappeared so rapidly,' said Pam. We both sat and watched her and I could not prevent a smug smile from spreading across my face. Her eyes narrowed as she noticed me:

'Look at Tia—I'm sure she knows what's happened.'

Graham turned towards me and I quickly adopted my most inscrutable expression. It was taking them longer than I expected to discover what animal had invaded Felicity and caused her to travel at a snail's pace. Of course, they did not have my sense of smell and for some time they were unable to name the culprit. When I had almost given up hope, Graham finally arrived at the correct answer.

'Ah I remember now. When I opened the garage this morning, a squirrel darted out as I lifted the door. I thought nothing of it at the time, but obviously it had been storing the bread in Felicity. I'm glad it escaped, otherwise we would have had a dead squirrel in the air filter as well as cubes of stale bread!'

Another incident concerning a squirrel could have proved fatal. It happened one cold morning when I was on Graham's desk, soaking up the weak sun slanting through the window as he worked. I became aware of movement outside on the terrace and, glancing out, saw Ziggy, looking like a mannequin wrapped in a coat with a massive fur collar strutting on a catwalk. As he paraded back and forth in front of the window, I instinctively knew that he needed help and jumped down—hurriedly pushing myself through the cat-flap to join him on the terrace.

'What in the world are you doing?' I shrieked as my fur began to stand on end.

Through clenched teeth that were sunk deep into the neck of an animal, he muttered. 'It's a squirrel and if I let go it will bite me. Get help quickly.'

Racing back into the house, I found Graham still sitting at his desk and I paced up and down emitting my loudest banshee until he was forced to look up.

'Be quiet, Tia, I'm working—stop that dreadful racket!' I wondered why humans were always so slow to react and why Graham had not realised that my loud and urgent signals were to get his attention. Eventually, my persistence was rewarded and he turned to me and demanded:

'What's the matter Tia, has something happened?' I continued to wail until he reluctantly rose from his chair saying: 'Is it Ziggy?'

Finally, I had achieved some action; Graham followed me as I abandoned my normal seductive strut and led him quickly to the terrace, where he immediately spotted Ziggy—still wearing his live fur collar.

'Good heavens', he cried, 'what on earth have you got there? Let me have a look old chap.'

Ziggy growled through his teeth.

'Ah! I see the problem—hold still, I must act quickly.'

With that, he took off his shoe and hit the tenacious squirrel on the head, stunning it instantly. Ziggy released the limp body and rushed to me for comfort while Graham disposed of it. I felt Ziggy trembling as I licked his head to calm him.

'Mum I was so frightened,' he cried.

'I know, so was I. Grey squirrels are vicious creatures and a bite would almost certainly have gone septic. How did it happen? I thought I told you to keep away from them.'

'Yes, I know, but I was climbing a tree and didn't notice it because it was the same colour as the bark. As soon as I spotted it, I started to climb down but the wretched thing chased me and attacked me when we reached the ground. I sprang at it and got a good grip on its neck, but it retaliated by curling itself round my throat trying to strangle me.'

'Well, it's over now so we can forget it, but let it be a lesson to you.'

'Yes, Mum, thank you for getting help—I couldn't have held on much longer,' he said, with his fur still stark after his frightening experience.

Many animals and birds visited us. One Sunday Ziggy and I were left in the house while the family went to church. Naturally, we made the most of the opportunity and played hide and seek together, racing from room to room and diving into cupboards. Upstairs we slid under the beds and pulled ourselves along on our backs by digging our claws into the canvas underneath, leaving strands hanging in loops as evidence of our activity. We hoped that no one would ever look underneath and see the extent of the damage—but we had great fun and it was good exercise.

We heard Felicity coming up the drive and, by the time she scrunched to a halt on the gravel forecourt, we were sitting watching from the window looking angelic. As the four of them stepped from the car, an enormous black bird swooped down from the parapet and alighted on the gravel in front of them. It strutted around on huge clawed feet and then started to speak:

'Hello, hello,' it said.

We sat watching, absolutely mesmerised. It seemed that the family were also transfixed, because they remained motionless while it continued to walk round them saying:

'Hello, how are you?'

If only Graham had let us out we would soon have chased it off—the two of us were quite formidable when it came to defending our territory. As it was, we could do nothing. Suddenly the bird made a dart at Claire and started to peck at her bare ankles.

'Oh!' she cried, 'that really hurt.'

Graham snapped out of his trance: 'This is too much, let's get indoors quickly,' he said, running towards the front door with the key ready to put into the lock.

The bird continued to circle the rest of the group occasionally pecking at their feet.

'Hurry Daddy,' Claire cried. 'Its beak is very sharp and it's getting more menacing.'

'Good morning, good morning,' said the bird. Then, tired of attacking them, it flew a short distance to one of a pair of stone urns on pedestals at the entrance to the forecourt. As it prepared to land, its flailing wings unceremoniously sliced through some trailing lobelias, which cascaded to the ground like locks falling at the snip of a hairdresser's scissors. It landed heavily in the centre of the urn and completely demolished some ivy-leaved geraniums.

'Just look at that! I'll never be able to match that urn to the other one now,' said Pam in exasperation. Another thought then occurred to her and she added: 'I hope we can get inside the house soon, I've a chicken in the oven and it will be burned to a frazzle—the cats don't like it overdone!'

By then, Graham had reached the front door and hurriedly turned the key in the lock.

'Quickly, all of you, I'll hold the door open while you make a dash for it.'

All three raced for the door and Graham slammed it shut as soon as everyone was safely inside.

'Oh, that was quite terrifying!' said Claire, rubbing her ankles where they had been pecked. 'I'll just go upstairs and put some disinfectant on the broken skin.'

A moment or two later, we heard the bird battering at the front door and then attacking its reflection in the windows, beating its wings against the panes. Finally, it stood on the broad stone window ledge of the room into which we had retreated, peering in at us and continuously pecking at the glass—wherever we went, it soon came to the window and resumed its attack. We normally had no fear of birds and chased off any that were stupid enough to come too close, but this one was different and we cowered in the corner like everyone else.

'What is it?' asked Pam. 'I've never seen a bird as belligerent as that before and it can talk.'

'I think it must be a mynah bird,' said Graham. 'They can be trained to speak; it's probably escaped from someone living locally—I'll telephone the police to ask whether anybody has reported one missing.'

Graham left us for a few minutes to make the call and on his return told us that the police knew about a missing bird; they would give the owner our telephone number so that he could come and retrieve it.

The bird disappeared from our sight as it flew up towards the roof; Graham cautiously stepped outside and soon spotted it watching him from the parapet. At that moment, the telephone rang; it was the owner asking for directions on how to find us.

We all breathed a sigh of relief when we heard a car turning into the drive. Pam and Graham were already on the doorstep by the time a short, swarthy, sour-faced man in overalls got out. Graham was about to tell him of our horror at being attacked but, before he could open his mouth, the little man became quite aggressive. He had noticed us cats sitting at the window and he turned to address Graham—who still had one eye on the intruder perched on the roof.

'I hope those dratted cats haven't been frightening Minnie, she's a very sensitive and valuable bird,' said her owner in a harsh voice.

'I would have described her as antagonistic rather than sensitive; she attacked my daughter's ankles and demolished the flowers in that urn,' said Graham, eyeing the man with distaste.

'She must have been provoked—you should have talked to her quietly and given her some food,' was the reply.

'She did most of the talking, but she never mentioned that she was hungry!' retorted Graham.

'Go inside while I call her down. She'll not come if you stand there,' snapped the little man.

Graham considered objecting to his attitude, but decided that it would be better to say nothing. He turned and went back into the house while Minnie was coaxed down from the roof by her owner, secured in a large cage and put into the battered old car. The man then took his seat at the wheel and drove off without a word of thanks for the return of his bird or any apology for the havoc it had caused.

Ziggy watched from the safety of the windowsill as the car belched down the drive and disappeared through the gate; then he went out to investigate. He quickly picked up the scent of the mynah bird and proceeded to race round in circles with his nose glued to the ground tracing its every movement. Eventually, he leaped on to the denuded urn and sat gazing at the family, who had gathered in the doorway to observe Minnie's departure with profound relief.

When he realised that he had an audience, Ziggy decided that this was the moment for celebration—with one almighty banshee he jumped from the urn and headed for the lawn where he completed three laps, accompanied by several leaps and double somersaults, returning at tremendous speed through the cat-flap in time for lunch.

# 6. Alarms & Excursions

Our morning stroll before breakfast enabled us to snuff the air and forecast the weather for the day; Ziggy and I soon developed routines to suit all conditions. On fine days we wandered for miles enjoying the freedom of the open country but, no matter how far we had roamed, our acute hearing enabled us to detect the clatter of cups when the family took tea on the lawn and we would race back—no way were we going to miss out on our saucer of milk. Then we would amuse ourselves in the garden until it was time for our main meal of the day, followed by the pleasure of the evening when the family relaxed together. We would drape ourselves over them, dozing or listening to their conversation, until bedtime.

One of our favourite places on cold days was a plastic basket on top of the washing machine in the boiler room. It usually held clean laundry waiting to be ironed and presented an irresistible temptation. Unfortunately, we were sometimes stuck there for hours if someone shut the door—not knowing that two Siamese were sleeping hidden beneath the freshly washed clothes. On such occasions, a few powerful banshees in chorus were usually effective in securing our release.

Another popular spot on chilly days was the top of Pam's desk, where she had placed a thin foam pad topped with an assortment of old cashmere and lambswool sweaters, so that we could be near her while she worked. All Siamese love wool and some even bite holes in blankets if they have the chance; however, Ziggy and I were never guilty of such reprehensible behaviour. An advantage of curling up with Ziggy in this location was the ability to overhear most of Pam's telephone conversations. On one occasion, it was obvious that someone had enquired how we were.

'Oh, they're fine thank you. Ziggy had an adventure yesterday but all's well now,' said Pam.

I looked at Ziggy's beautiful sleek body sleeping peacefully beside me and remembered the incident the previous day when he had climbed a tree. Graham had collected Claire and Laura from the station and Ziggy, who had been waiting for them on a low stone wall near the courtyard, went wild with excitement when he saw them getting out of the car. In order to get their full attention and show them how pleased he was to see them, he started racing round and round the lawn leaping like a gazelle until, throwing caution to the wind, he sprang at a tall pine tree in the small copse behind the house. Scaling it nimbly, he climbed up to a branch where he paused and looked down to make sure that the family was assembled below watching him; then he let out a piercing wail on realising that he was much higher than he intended and far too frightened to descend.

'Idiotic cat,' Graham said. 'Sometimes I wonder whether he has a screw loose!'

'Don't be unkind,' remarked Pam. 'It's only because he was so excited at seeing the girls again.'

'Yes, but how stupid to climb so high. We'll have to try to get him down but my ladder won't extend that far. It's going to be difficult to rescue him.'

'Perhaps he'll come down on his own,' suggested Laura.

'Not a chance,' said Claire. 'Hang on—he's trying. Come on Ziggy!' she cried, to encourage him.

Ziggy moved very cautiously, facing the trunk of the tree as he slowly started to climb down backwards.

'That's right, come on,' they all chorused.

Ziggy then lost his nerve completely and, seeing a branch to his right, decided to walk along it rather than continue downwards. Unfortunately, most of the limb had been broken off in a storm and what remained was only a few feet long. He found that he could neither go forward nor turn round to come back.

I paced up and down, frantic with worry, knowing that, if he fell from that height, he could break every bone in his body.

'Daddy, there's a long boat hook in the garage; if we fastened a basket to it you might be able to hold it close enough for Ziggy to get in. Then we could lower him to the ground,' suggested Claire.

'I think it's doubtful,' was the reply, 'but we could try.'

The boat hook was brought and the basket was attached and raised up to Ziggy who looked at it and emitted another howl. Everyone tried to persuade him to get in but he remained glued to his branch, paralysed with fear.

'No, it's no good; we'll have to think of something else,' said Laura. 'What about getting a large sheet and persuading him to jump into it?'

'Yes, we could try that,' Graham replied.

There are some dust sheets in one of the drawers in the utility room,' said Pam.

While Laura went for an old sheet, I stared up at Ziggy and felt sick with fear.

The sheet was brought and unfolded; each member of the family then grasped a corner firmly and stretched it out tautly at the base of the tree.

'Jump, Ziggy, jump!' everyone called in unison. However, Ziggy was having none of it and I knew that now was the time for me to intervene.

'Come on, darling,' I cried. 'The sheet's very large and if you let go and drop into the centre you'll be quite all right.'

'Mum, Mum, I'm so frightened—it's such a long way down,' he wailed.

'I know,' I replied, 'but if you do what they tell you, you'll be fine.'

'Won't they be angry, perhaps they'll smack me?'

'I'm sure they won't, they never have and in any case they'll be too relieved that you're safe. Come on now, just screw up your courage, close your eyes, and let go,' I cajoled.

'It's obvious that he can't or won't jump,' said Graham. 'I shall have to give him a good sharp prod with the end of the boat-hook while the three of you hold the sheet as best you can.'

Graham climbed the ladder and extended the boat-hook out towards Ziggy while the others held the sheet about three feet from the ground. When Ziggy saw the boat-hook advancing towards him, he stepped back away from it and, feeling that he was in danger of falling, shifted his grip on the branch, lost his balance and ended hanging upside down—clinging like a monkey.

'Come on Daddy, you'll have to give him a really good jab now so that he'll let go and drop into the sheet,' said Claire.

Graham raised the boat-hook again and gave Ziggy another prod, which so startled him that he released his grip and came hurtling downwards. As I watched, my heart beating at an alarming rate, I saw him instinctively twist his head to protect his chin with his front paws, then rotate the remainder of his body until he was the right way up, keeping his hind legs bent and back arched to absorb his impact on landing. It was quite remarkable to watch the precision and coordination of his actions in so short a time.

Everyone waited expectantly for Ziggy to bounce up from the sheet like a gymnast on a trampoline—instead, there was a loud renting noise as the sheet tore and Ziggy disappeared through the hole. On reaching the ground, he merely shook himself and started to walk nonchalantly away—with nothing apparently hurt, apart from his pride.

I rushed to him. 'What a narrow squeak; you certainly lost one of your nine lives then!' I said as I kissed him. I could see that he was really shaken and sorry that he had very nearly turned the joyous occasion of the girls' homecoming into a major disaster. However, perhaps it had taught him a lesson and he would think twice before climbing so high again.

'Just look at them,' said Claire. 'Aren't they wonderful together—I'm sure Tia really loves him.'

Of course, I loved him; he was my son and I had loved his father too. The remembrance of Ben and the trauma of the recent events made me suddenly feel very sad and I crept under a rhododendron bush to relieve my pent-up emotions.

When we first arrived, we were allowed to roam freely inside the house at night, but this was brought to an abrupt end by an incident late one evening after the family had gone to bed. We had been playing our favourite indoor game, usually reserved as a celebration at the departure of unwelcome guests, which involves circumnavigating the sitting room at high speed, without touching the floor. On this occasion, Ziggy became very excited as he flew round the room from chair to chair and then—just to be different—decided to leap on to the mantelpiece. All hell was let loose as a deafening noise, akin to the climax of a James Bond film, shook the house. A klaxon pulsed great blasts of sound outside, while a siren wailed continuously in the hall. Infrared beams had been strategically placed to set off alarms if burglars broke in to the house. We were normally well below these invisible beams, but Ziggy had interrupted one of them by his athletic jump on to the mantelpiece.

The cacophony had a drastic effect on Ziggy, who was completely disorientated by the racket; he jumped down and cowered behind one of the armchairs, shivering with fright. I, too, was shaken by the piercing noise, but managed to pull myself together sufficiently to go to him and comfort him by licking his head.

On hearing the deafening din, the family came running down the stairs, hastily pulling on dressing gowns. The alarm system was switched off, the noise ceased, and every door and window was examined for signs of illegal entry. When none was found suspicion fell on us—several cushions scattered around the floor of the sitting room soon confirmed our guilt.

Graham discovered us hiding behind the chair and said: 'Ah, there you are—what did you think you were doing at this time of night?'

We crawled forward on our bellies and nuzzled Graham to beg forgiveness. He relented, as we knew he would, but thereafter we were always shut in his study at night.

There was a window behind the desk in Graham's study with a blind, which was seldom pulled down in the evening because its main purpose was to shield the computer screen from bright afternoon sunlight. After the family had gone to bed, Ziggy and I used to sit side by side on the desk and gaze out of the window. It was a wonderful vantage point, giving us a panoramic view of most of the rear garden. A stone-flagged terrace ran the length of the house and beyond it the main lawn stretched away to a long herbaceous border. A clipped yew hedge separated the border from a grass tennis court and a taller hedge, beyond the court, hid a fence marking the boundary of our property.

The lawn sloped gently upwards, enabling us to see anything walking along in the moonlight. We frequently watched lean and mangy foxes creeping stealthily through the grounds; I was thankful that we were safely behind glass when I saw one carrying a very large rabbit. The foxes were often very noisy; the sharp high-pitched triple bark of the male and the vixen's wailing screams could be quite blood-curdling at night. We also observed the antics of mice and squirrels and even some badgers, who had burrowed under our wire fence from their set in the adjacent grounds.

One morning I awoke early, left my basket and jumped onto the desk. From this observation point, I noticed that a young deer had leaped over the five-bar gate into the garden. I roused Ziggy who joined me, still rubbing the sleep from his eyes, and we were both horrified to watch it casually stripping the leaves and buds from Graham's beautiful pink Queen Elizabeth roses, which were growing in a bed at the edge of the lawn. They were his pride and joy and he had spent many hours fertilising, pruning and spraying them—eagerly awaiting the moment when they reached their prime. We knew that he would be heartbroken when he saw the damage the deer was causing, so we tried to alert the family by howling in unison—but they remained fast asleep. Ziggy and I continued yelling our loudest, hoping to scare the deer away, but it took no notice until we rattled the window in its frame with our paws. The sudden loud noise frightened it and, clearing the gate with the ease of a champion hurdler, it bounded off at great speed.

When Graham came downstairs to let us out of his study for our morning stroll before breakfast, we induced him to follow us and led him quickly to the border. He was appalled to see what had happened to his treasured bushes, many of which were almost bare while most of the others had broken or missing shoots. Dozens of small prints in the soft soil left him in no doubt regarding the perpetrator of the damage. We returned sadly to the house leaving Graham surveying the scene of desecration; he, of course, was completely unaware that our prompt action had prevented it from being worse.

The long herbaceous border was planted with hundreds of perennial plants, which had been carefully chosen to ensure that it was colourful for most of the year. We found it a wonderful place for making nests in which to lie and enjoy the sun and also for playing hide and seek.

Ziggy soon discovered that the border held another attraction in the form of a large clump of catnip. He would take a few short sniffs and then roll on his back, flattening the plant and biting frantically at any strands that were near enough to his face. Then he would leap into the air and crash down into the centre of the clump, making curious chunnering noises and rubbing himself against the leaves—finally lying on his back for some time with a stupefied expression on his face. I could never understand why he experienced such a powerful reaction to catnip; it did nothing for me and I even found the smell rather unpleasant. Fortunately, his drug habit seemed to have no lasting effect and he would return to normal within a few minutes of leaving the border.

Although we had a large garden, we liked to visit the neighbouring ones—even if we were not always welcome. One of our favourite pastimes involved teasing a Dalmatian called Polka who lived next door; she normally had the run of her garden but was chained to her kennel when the gate was open. This was the opportunity for us to scramble under the hedge and stroll arrogantly across the lawn towards the tethered dog—flaunting ourselves in front of her in the knowledge that she could not reach us. At the sight of us, Polka would charge forward barking furiously, only to be jerked to an abrupt halt by her chain. She would work herself up into a frenzy of frustration as we sat, just out of range, and gave ourselves a long slow wash—blatantly ignoring her frantic attempts to break free.

We thought this was enormous fun until one day, as we reached the centre of her lawn, we were flabbergasted to

see her spring from her kennel and race towards us completely unrestrained. We knew instinctively that it could be fatal to turn and run; so we stood broadside to her, our legs stiff and our spines arched like two croquet hoops, raising the fur on our backs and tails and swearing threateningly. Polka, who had expected us to flee for our lives and was already anticipating the thrill of the chase, was completely bewildered by our extraordinary stance and terrifying appearance. Fearful of having her nose slashed by our sharp claws, she stopped dead in her tracks, whimpered and retreated to her kennel.

I suppose our behaviour was inexcusable, but all Siamese have a wicked streak in their make-up. However, our narrow squeak taught us a lesson and we never played that game again, always skirting round the edge of Polka's boundary under cover of the rhododendron bushes whenever we entered her territory.

We were playing innocently in our own garden when a young woman, who lived locally, walked up the drive pushing a smart pram. Pam opened the door in response to her ring on the bell.

'Hello,' she said, 'I'm Susan, my mother told me that you'd like to see my baby, so I thought I would drop in as I happened to be passing.'

'Yes, please come in. I'd love to see the new arrival.'

Susan lifted the baby out of the pram and the three of them disappeared into the house. We had been watching with interest, hidden behind some bushes; as soon as the door was closed, we advanced to take a closer look at the empty pram.

While crossing the gravelled drive, some small stones became stuck between the pads of my paws and I had to sit down to extract them; meanwhile Ziggy had reached the pram. He sniffed at each wheel as he walked around it, finally resting his front paws on top of one of them, while craning his neck upwards in order to examine the interior—his head like a cabbage on the end of a stalk. Then, as curiosity overcame him, he jumped inside and called to me:

'Come and see, Mum—I've never been in a pram before, it's very warm and comfortable.'

It was a long way up and I crouched on the ground wiggling my bottom several times as I judged the distance before I leaped into the pram—setting it rocking as I landed almost on top of Ziggy. It certainly was exceptionally cosy and smelled of baby powder and warm wool—an ideal place for an afternoon snooze. We snuggled together underneath the soft blanket and were soon fast asleep.

When Susan left the house, she carried her baby to the pram. Holding the infant in one arm, she pulled back the blanket with the other and gave a horrified scream at the sight of us, curled up with our tails wound round our noses—we might have been two venomous snakes rather than a pair of delightful Siamese! Awakened sharply by the swift removal of the blanket, we both swore at her, leaped out and raced for cover—leaving Pam to make profuse apologies for our behaviour.

Many of our games were not so malicious or naughty—some were just plain fun. From the start of spring, the lawns needed cutting once a week. We loved the smell and soft feel of the freshly cut grass and derived endless pleasure from burrowing into a huge pile of clippings, which Graham enlarged whenever the box attached to his ride-on mower became full to overflowing.

We would hide inside the heap of cuttings until we heard the sound of the mower's engine die down to a soft throb as he stopped to remove the grass box. When he started to empty it on to the heap, we would jump out like a couple of Jack-in-the-boxes trying to startle him. He would join in the fun and pretend to be cross, chasing us around until we attempted to hide from him by burying our bodies in the clippings—although we knew that he could still see our exposed tails twitching with excitement as we waited to be discovered and petted. These antics would continue until the mowing was completed, by which time we would all be totally exhausted and ready for tea.

The freshly mown grass was the signal for a game of croquet. Pam and Graham would comb the lawn searching for the holes from which the hoops had been removed to allow free passage for the mower. Once they were all back in place, the balls and mallets would be taken from a long wooden box and battle commenced.

There is nothing dull about a normal game of croquet—even the most tranquil player can explode with fury when an opponent displaces the ball he has perfectly aligned for the next hoop. The addition of mobile hazards in the form of two Siamese cats blocking hoops or deflecting balls from their intended path can arouse terrible passions—even the local vicar gave vent to a blasphemous expletive when Ziggy put out a paw and deliberately sabotaged his shot—which would certainly have gone through the hoop had it not been intercepted.

Ziggy's dislike of the vicar stemmed from the fact that the legs of his trousers smelled strongly of his dog. Ziggy found this so offensive that he would stand with mouth open, tongue partly protruding and nose wrinkled, sneering at the strong canine scent—occasionally glancing over his shoulder to make sure that the assembled company witnessed his performance.

The games of croquet were sometimes so exciting that they continued well into the evening. One lasted until it was almost dark and torches had to be brought out to illuminate the strip of lawn in front of a ball while a lantern silhouetted the hoop at which the player was aiming.

When the winner hit the peg and the game was finally over, we would jump in and out of the wooden box while the mallets were replaced and then make our way back across the dew-soaked lawn to the warmth of the house. These were halcyon days and we both derived tremendous pleasure from being part of the family.

# 7. Bleak House

Sylvia and Peter, some friends who lived about sixty miles away, invited Pam and Graham to a party and suggested that they stayed overnight. This created a problem because we were never left alone at night and both girls had previous engagements in London. All attempts to find an alternative cat sitter failed, so Graham telephoned Peter to reluctantly decline the invitation.

'Don't worry, we love cats—particularly Siamese. You're very welcome to bring them with you,' was the reply.

On the appointed day, Pam and Graham loaded the car with their small overnight bag, our litter tray, our baskets and blankets, our feeding bowls, our food for the evening meal and breakfast the following morning, our collars and leads and Ziggy's favourite catnip mouse.

When we reached the attractive cottage, Peter, a tall good-looking man with finely chiselled features, came out to greet us with an anxious face.

'I'm so sorry—we have a problem. My uncle and aunt have arrived unexpectedly and commandeered our spare bedroom. I tried to call you on the telephone but you'd already left, so I've reserved a room for you at a local hotel—the only one for miles around. It would be a good idea to book in right away, so that you'll have time to change. I hope it won't be too uncomfortable—we've never been inside but I'm afraid it was Hobson's choice. We were looking forward to having you stay with us and the children are particularly disappointed because they could hardly contain their excitement at the thought of playing with the cats when they woke up in the morning.'

'Don't worry about it,' said Pam; while Graham turned the car to head back in the direction we had come. 'We'll see you later.'

Ziggy and I stared apprehensively out of the car window as we approached a gloomy building on the outskirts of the nearby village. Graham read out a faded notice at the gate. 'BLAKE'S GUEST HOUSE—BED & BREAKFAST—NO PETS.'

'Oh dear!' said Pam. 'What are we going to do now?'

'Ignore it, we'll just go in and register,' Graham answered.

He hardly had time to switch off the ignition before a daunting woman appeared in the doorway and walked towards the car. She was singularly unattractive and even her futile attempt at a smile only made her look grotesque, but this small semblance of warmth evaporated instantly when she looked into the car and saw the two of us sitting on the back seat.

We shrank back in horror, not just at the sight of her hostile face but because a large white bull terrier accompanied her; it sniffed at the car and then, panting from exertion, heaved itself up and looked in at us with eyes that betrayed near blindness. We were revolted by its discoloured tongue and yellow fangs as it growled and slobbered over the clean glass—leaving us in no doubt concerning our fate if it ever managed to reach us.

Without even a hint of politeness and forgoing all basic formalities, the woman rasped at Graham.

'Didn't you see the sign? I won't have any animals in the house because they upset Titan—those cats must remain where they are,' she stated, in a voice that invited no argument.

We cowered in the car while Pam and Graham went up to their room to change. Their mood when they returned was decidedly gloomy and they drove back to the cottage in almost total silence—except for a few moans from us, which were totally ignored.

The atmosphere changed when we arrived at the party and were taken to a small comfortable room next to the kitchen; quickly showing our appreciation when we were given sample scraps from the elaborate buffet, including prawns, smoked salmon and even a little caviar—which Ziggy rejected because he lacked my refined taste.

The party was initially fairly subdued as guests exchanged polite greetings but, as the evening progressed, alcohol released their inhibitions and loosened their tongues. Once the music started, the noise reached such a crescendo that people had to shout to make themselves heard. It was a very successful party and Ziggy and I were warm and snug, undisturbed by the dancing feet and loud voices; but occasionally I found myself thinking about the dreary guest house and our impending night in the cold car.

Some hours later, we heard the sound of guests departing and footsteps in the corridor.

'Come along you two,' said Graham poking his head round the door. 'We must be off now—quite a few of the others have gone and we don't want to be the last to leave.'

He picked us up, one under each arm, and walked through the house to the car where Pam was waiting to open the rear door for us.

'I'll just get their basket and then we must say good-bye to everybody.'

He returned with the basket, which he put in the boot, and together they walked to the porch where Sylvia and Peter were bidding everyone goodnight.

'It was a lovely party, thank you both so much. Tia and Ziggy also greatly enjoyed themselves—they haven't eaten so many prawns in their lives.'

'Thank you for coming,' our host replied. 'So sorry about the spare room but I hope you'll be comfortable in the village.'

'I'm sure we'll be fine,' called Graham as he and Pam got into the car.

Several other guests were also heading for their transport, some of them rather inebriated, and one of them stumbled against the side of our car as he tried to find his own among the many cluttering the driveway.

'Sorry,' he said, 'can't remember where my wife parked the thing.' Then, glancing behind Graham to the back seat where we were sitting, he exclaimed in a voice loud enough to wake the whole neighbourhood: 'Oh, what beautiful Siamese! Come and look everyone!'

Normally, I love being admired and acknowledged as beautiful, but not by a man in a drunken stupor. What was worse, when the other guests heard him call out they surrounded the car, peering in through the windows, leering and making what they imagined to be cat noises at us. Graham could not move because many of them were leaning heavily against the car to support themselves and would have fallen over had he driven off.

I could hardly believe that these were the same people who, only a few hours earlier, had graced the party with their refined small talk and prissy gestures; their conversation now consisted of loud laughter and high-pitched squawks, and I noticed that Ziggy was trembling with fear. I had never seen people in this condition before and felt embarrassed for them. Fortunately, Peter realised that things were getting out of hand and broke up the group by calling out:

'Goodnight everyone, time to go home; mind how you drive.'

The crowd reluctantly shifted its weight from the car as Graham started the engine. I breathed a sigh of relief when the fatuous faces and groping hands disappeared from our view as we turned out of the drive and headed down the road towards the hotel.

Graham had nicknamed our destination Bleak House and it certainly contrasted with the luxury and warmth of the cottage we had just left. He had been given a key because we would be late back and, when we reached the gloomy house, we found a single dim light burning in the hallway—making the place look even more dismal than before.

By our plaintive cries, Pam and Graham sensed that we were frightened of sleeping in the car—the grim hotel would be preferable so long as we could be with them.

'No way will we leave you both outside all night, so you must be very quiet and help us to smuggle you upstairs,' Pam reassured us.

Their plan was simple. Graham borrowed a clothesline, from the yard at the side of the hotel, and Pam carried it up to their bedroom to lower it from the window. Then

Graham attached the line to the handle of our basket so that we could be hauled up to their room.

All went well initially but, just after Graham had fastened the line to the basket and was heading for the house, the lights in the lounge were switched on and the dangling clothesline was clearly visible through the uncurtained window. Graham reacted quickly and went to the door of the lounge to distract the attention of the awesome woman and her faithful hound—who were investigating the noise of our arrival. He engaged her in conversation while, over her shoulder, he watched us slowly ascending in our improvised lift—our faces peering anxiously through the wire door of our basket.

The bull terrier, though nearly blind, retained an excellent sense of smell. It swayed its huge head from side to side until it established a precise fix on Graham's location—then it charged. Graham stepped sideways and the dog hurtled through the open doorway, crashing with a thud against the wall of the hallway; meanwhile Pam quickly pulled us up out of sight.

Safe in the bedroom, Ziggy and I curled up comfortably at the end of the bed and settled for the night. We must have been asleep for about an hour, when a long roll of thunder awakened us and lightning briefly illuminated the room, while torrential rain hammered at the window. Ziggy jumped down from the bed and searched high and low; eventually disappearing under a large wardrobe from which he emerged covered from head to tail in fluff and dust—resembling a bush of old-man's-beard. After he had recovered from a fit of sneezing, I tried to clean him up as best I could.

Then came the question I had been dreading: 'Mum, where's my pan?'

Unfortunately, our essential litter tray had been completely overlooked during the operation to smuggle us upstairs; it always travelled everywhere with us and at that moment was on the floor of the car, which was parked in the yard at the side of the house. Ziggy started to make urgent noises. If only the accommodation had included an en-suite bathroom, there would have been no problem since I had seen Ziggy poised over the plughole of Pam's bath on many occasions. However, our room lacked any such refinement.

Pam woke and took charge of the situation. 'Graham, I think Ziggy needs his pan. I know it's pouring with rain but you'll have to fetch it; he would be absolutely mortified if he had an accident—he's neurotic enough as it is!'

Graham slipped a raincoat over his pyjamas to brave the downpour and fetch our portable loo. A long time elapsed before he returned and Ziggy was by then nearly demented. Suddenly the door opened and Graham entered with water dripping from his nose and hair; his coat saturated by the heavy rain. Ziggy streaked to the pan as soon as it touched the floor.

'Where have you been?' asked Pam. 'I was beginning to think you'd met the owner again.'

'No, it wasn't that,' replied Graham. 'In my rush to get back to Ziggy, I grabbed the pan and caught my sleeve on the handle of the car door, spilling nearly all of the litter into a puddle. I had to search for some dry earth to replace it and got soaked to the skin. When I returned to the house, I couldn't remember which was our room because all the doors are identical. Unfortunately, I picked the wrong one and marched in—much to the bewilderment of an old lady in a buttercup yellow nightdress with her hair in curlers. She sat bolt upright in her bed when a flash of lightning illuminated me framed in the open doorway—with water running down my face, a trowel in one hand and a tray of earth in the other. Before she had time to scream, I retreated closing the door behind me. I waited for her shrieks but there was total silence—she probably thought that she'd imagined the whole incident.'

After drying himself off, Graham climbed back into bed while we pawed continuously at the bedclothes until our persistence was rewarded and we were allowed into the bed. We were still asleep when there was a knock on the door and the fearsome owner appeared, carrying a tray of tea. Ziggy and I rose with one accord from under the sheets and directed a stream of Siamese oaths at her. She was so shocked that she dropped the tray on to the dressing table and ran from the room—leaving us sitting on the bed smirking triumphantly.

Pam and Graham dressed hastily, skipped the breakfast for which they had been forced to pay in advance, and bundled us into the car. We were relieved when the engine responded to the first turn of the key and we quickly set off on the homeward journey, during which we slept peacefully—content in the knowledge that we would soon be back in our own familiar surroundings.

# 8. The Cattery

After dinner one evening, when we were all sitting comfortably together, the question of a holiday was discussed; naturally, Ziggy and I listened intently to the conversation.

'Have you any idea where you would like to go?' Graham asked Pam.

'I would love to visit Mallorca again,' she replied. 'We could look up some of the friends we made while we were there on our honeymoon. I know it's become quite built-up in places, but most of the island is still very beautiful and, if we hired a car, we could see some of the areas we never had time to explore—unlike thirty years ago, travel is much easier now and it would be quite economical if we booked a package holiday.'

Ziggy and I looked at one another—where in the world was Mallorca and what would happen to us while they were away? These were our unspoken questions and we did not have long to wait for the answers.

'What about the cats? They can't go to Spain with us.'

Now we knew that Mallorca was in Spain and we assumed that it must be a considerable distance away if they were unable to take us with them.

'They'll have to go to a cattery; I believe there's quite a good one about five miles away,' said Graham.

'They won't like that!' was the reply.

'Well, do you or don't you want a holiday?' said Graham testily. 'Heaven knows I could use one right now; my workload this year has been very heavy but things are reasonably quiet at the moment and I could spare a fortnight. The cats will be perfectly all right, you worry far too much about them, after all they'll be together and that's the main thing.'

Once their flight was booked, we waited apprehensively for the day of their departure. For some weeks, nothing happened and we began to hope that they had changed their plans. However, when they took their suitcases from the cupboards and laid out their clothes on the bed, it was obvious that their holiday was imminent.

'Mum, if we hide somewhere in the garden where they can't find us, we won't have to go to the cattery,' Ziggy suggested.

'I just wish we could, darling, but we couldn't fend for ourselves for a fortnight and one of the mangy foxes might get us. We're used to sleeping in a warm comfortable basket together and we rely on food being brought to us— apart from the titbits we catch ourselves. If it were just for two nights, we might risk it; but a fortnight is a long time and, if we were missing, they would worry about us and probably cancel their holiday. At least if we go to the cattery we'll be safe.'

In due course, we commenced the journey to our temporary prison with both of us protesting vociferously from the back seat.

'Don't they make an infernal racket,' Graham said. 'How can I concentrate on driving with that noise going on behind me? It doesn't seem possible that two small cats can make such a din and keep it up for so long.'

'Be quiet, both of you! You'll only make your throats sore and you're going whether you like it or not,' ordered Pam.

The journey continued, with us now complaining spasmodically, until we reached our destination.

Our quarters comprised the usual pen with a wooden shed in one corner. The pen was completely enclosed by wire netting, including the top, from which I assumed that it had housed some acrobatic cats in its time. Twenty or so similar pens were ranged on either side of a concrete path; a gate at the end was always carefully closed after use during the day and padlocked at night. Some of the occupants were extremely valuable, while others were much-loved pets—so security was very tight.

In the distance, there were four or five much larger breeding pens with more elaborate sheds and grass runs—unlike our uncomfortable concrete one. Somehow, it all seemed slightly familiar. Could this have been where I had met Ben? I decided to ask a beautiful female blue-point Siamese who was preening herself in the adjoining pen.

'Excuse me, I think that I may have been to this cattery before and I wonder if you know whether there is a male seal-point Siamese here, called Ben?'

'I've no idea. This is my first visit and I hope it's my last. My owners wouldn't listen to the strong objections I made and left me here while they went abroad. My name is Sapphire by the way—what's yours?'

'I'm Tia Maria and this is my son, Ziggy; Ben is his father,' I replied.

'Wow! What do you know! No wonder you were enquiring after him. What a lovely boy your son is.'

'Yes, his father is very handsome, lithe and muscular with dark blue eyes. He's also very charming and we found that we had quite a lot to talk about—we really got on well together,' I said.

'You were lucky,' said Sapphire. 'The only time I was taken to meet a male it ended in disaster; he frightened me to death when I was put in with him and naturally I clawed and scratched him. The owner of the cattery was so worried that her precious cat would be scarred for life that I was packed off home and my owners were told never to bring me back. I'm expecting to be sent somewhere else fairly soon, but I won't be quite so nervous next time.'

'Who occupies the pen next to yours? Perhaps they've been here before and will remember Ben.'

'Not a chance. He's a real bruiser with no manners whatsoever and doesn't want to be friendly. I did try to talk to him when I first arrived, but it was useless because he has no conversation at all—his language is appalling and full of swear words. He hasn't an inkling of how to behave and I have no option but to try to avoid him,' Sapphire replied. 'I'm sorry, Tia, I really wish I could help you. Why not ask the chap next to you on the other side?'

'I haven't seen anyone there yet; he must be asleep inside the shed. When he appears, I'll introduce myself and see what he has to say.'

At that moment, Ziggy sidled up to me holding a paw in front of his nose.

'Mum, what's that dreadful smell? It's got right to the back of my throat and my eyes are starting to water.'

'That's only disinfectant,' I answered. 'In a place like this, it's necessary to keep everything as clean as possible; the pens are swilled out every day with a strong solution so that germs can't multiply.'

'But I don't have any germs,' he cried.

'I know, darling, but every precaution has to be taken because some of the cats who stay here are worth a fortune and their owners would sue the cattery if they became ill.'

'I don't like it here, I want to go home,' Ziggy wailed.

'Stop that, Ziggy; you're making me feel miserable too. Please put on a brave face and sit this out for a fortnight. Come on now, let's have a game of *I Spy*, you know you like that.'

After half-an-hour, we had exhausted most of the things we could see from our confined quarters and it was then I noticed that the occupant of the pen on our other side had come out into the afternoon sunshine and was snuffing the air.

'Why, hello!' he said. 'I thought I heard voices. I was just taking a nap; it helps to pass the time if I sleep a lot. Isn't it hot?'

He was a large cat; a beautiful blue Persian with amber coloured eyes. No wonder he was hot; his sumptuous dense fur had become slightly matted from only superficial grooming during his stay in the cattery.

'Good afternoon, my name is Tia Maria and this is my son Ziggy,' I replied.

'How do you do, my name is Charles—damn silly name for a Persian, but there you are. How long are you staying?' he enquired.

'For a fortnight, our family has gone to Spain and we're both feeling homesick already. Ziggy doesn't like being cooped up and he's finding it very frustrating. I'm trying to calm him as best I can but it's not easy.'

'Youths of today are not very tolerant. When I was young, we took things as they came and didn't question everything. Nowadays they complain of boredom unless they're doing exactly what they want.'

'Ziggy is usually very good; he lets off steam occasionally but he's a loving and obedient son.'

'You're lucky to have him with you; I've never seen any of my offspring—I don't even know how many I have,' he remarked sadly.

Now seemed to be an appropriate moment to put my question to him.

'Do you know whether a Siamese called Ben lives here?'

'What a small world!' he exclaimed. 'In your pen last week there was a young seal-point Siamese; she was only here for one night and her owners collected her the following day. During that time she told me her life story; I couldn't stop her talking and what tales she had to tell! She really was a little minx and she kept me up half the night with her anecdotes. However, the point is that she mentioned Ben as one of her suitors and described him as a handsome fellow with tremendous charm—but he doesn't live here.'

'Yes, that sounds like my Ben; I found him absolutely fascinating and I'm still in love with him—Ziggy is his son.'

'Well, he's a fine lad and I can see why you're so proud of him. I'm stuck here for several weeks and if there's anything I can do, please let me know. I exercise every morning and perhaps Ziggy would like to join me; it helps pass the time and keeps the body supple. We could even run races up and down our pens—although with those long legs, he would probably beat me easily.'

This struck me as a good idea.

'Thank you, that's very kind. I'm sure he'd be delighted to work out with you.'

I called to Ziggy—now in the process of trying to climb up to the wire-netting roof. 'Darling, Charles has very kindly invited you to do exercises with him tomorrow. Would you like that?'

'Yes, I should.' Ziggy climbed down, walked over to the wire separating the two pens, and addressed Charles: 'Thank you for your offer, I don't know any exercises but it would be fun if you could teach me some.'

The matter was settled and I was delighted that Ziggy would be occupied—it would take his mind off feeling homesick.

Sapphire and I became great friends; we spent long hours talking to one another while Charles and Ziggy invented more and more exercises and games to play together.

One loses all sense of time in a cattery, probably because so many hours are spent sleeping. However, early one morning, before the cleaners had been in to do the chores with their mops and clanking buckets, I heard a familiar voice calling us.

'T-i-a, Z-i-g-g-y—Where are you?'

We leaped through the cat-flap screaming loudly and desperately trying to see if it really were Pam.

'We're here, we're here,' we chorused.

At that moment, we heard an authoritarian voice command: 'Madam, you are not to go near the cats until you have been to the office!'

'But I must just see them,' Pam cried.

'No-one is allowed to enter the pen area except staff.'

We could hear Pam protesting but she could do nothing except wait for us to be brought to her. The minutes

seemed interminable while the formalities were concluded.

At last, we were handed over and put in the car for the journey home. Graham drove while Pam talked to us continuously as we sat and purred on the back seat.

'My darlings, I hope you were well looked after and weren't too miserable. Never mind, it wasn't for very long and we won't be going away again for some time.'

The car turned into the drive and, as we approached the house, we saw the girls waiting to greet us in the doorway—they had collected their parents from the airport the night before. As soon as the car door was opened, Ziggy burst out like a greyhound from a trap, let out one almighty yell of delight, and started to race round and round the lawn.

'That cat really is mad!' Claire exclaimed.

'No, he's just excited and pleased to be home. It must have been awful for him to be cooped up because he's so high-spirited. How different from when he first arrived and was so nervous that even someone rolling up a newspaper frightened him to death,' remarked Laura, glancing affectionately towards him.

The family strolled slowly around the garden, inspecting the progress the plants had made in their absence.

'Look how much the lawn has grown,' said Graham. 'I shall have to get the mower out tomorrow; I'm sure there are plenty of things that'll need doing in the house today. You go on in and I'll collect the luggage from the car.'

When he noticed that everyone had gone inside, Ziggy ended his acrobatic exhibition, ran round the house and crashed through the cat-flap. He joined me and we sat listening in fascination while the two girls were given a full account of their parents' holiday in Mallorca.

# 9. The Invisible Man

It was wonderful to be home and life quickly returned to normal. As it was still summer, we spent most of the time outside and both Ziggy and I had favourite spots in the garden where we would spend hours basking in the sun.

Most of our meals were taken inside the house, but afternoon tea was usually served on the lawn alongside a tall yew hedge. An extra saucer was always put on the tray for us and we would appear as soon as we heard the sound of the teacups.

Ziggy often chose that moment to spring from beneath the hedge and bowl me over and over. It was his idea of a game and he thought it very amusing, but it exasperated me because I felt it was beneath my dignity to be knocked off my feet.

'That's enough, Ziggy,' I would remonstrate.

'Stop it, Ziggy,' Pam would say. 'Just leave your mother in peace to enjoy her milk.'

A saucer would be put down for us and we would lap happily until it was empty. We would wait patiently for it to be replenished but, if she happened to be deep in conversation with Graham and failed to notice that we had finished, it was necessary for us to ask.

'Oh dear, wasn't I quick enough for you,' Pam would say as she refilled the saucer. 'I was told when you first came that neither of you liked milk, but just look at you now!'

After we had emptied the saucer for the second time, we would settle down to wash ourselves. The edge of the lawn beside the yew hedge provided a lovely soft bank on which we could perform the necessary contortions to ensure that we reached every important part—taking particular care to clean our faces and whiskers thoroughly, as we did not want to smell of sour milk.

Once the ritual of afternoon tea was over, Pam and Graham would return to their respective desks and work through to the evening. We usually remained outside but would rush into the house if we heard a ring on the doorbell, since every caller had to be investigated. We would accompany whoever went to open the door but stood well back until we had ascertained who was there— only stepping forward to greet a visitor we recognised.

'Oh, aren't you lovely!' they would say. 'How are you both?'

'Fine,' we would reply in chorus as we followed them into the sitting room.

However, if it were a stranger, Ziggy would race upstairs, hide under one of the beds and not reappear until he was certain the coast was clear. My reaction was not quite so dramatic, although I would keep my distance— emitting my banshee at intervals in an attempt to cut short any conversation on the doorstep.

One day, we heard the doorbell and raced in at breakneck speed to hide behind Pam as she walked towards the front door. As she opened it, we were astounded to see a faceless man standing there. His large felt hat was pulled down almost to his ears, the brim barely clearing his eyebrows, while a thin aluminium mask with cut-outs for his nose and mouth held a square of cotton wadding, which completely obscured the rest of his features.

At the sight of him, I am ashamed to say that we both reacted very badly. Ziggy swore at him twice before racing upstairs and I pranced around on stiff legs, swearing and growling with the fur on my back rising to form a ridge and my tail fluffing out like a flue brush.

The man on the doorstep was equally startled; it was obvious that he had never previously seen a Siamese with its hackles roused. Pam was unworried, because she recognised him, despite his mask.

'I'm sorry for causing such a commotion; once I'm indoors, I can take this thing off—but I suffer dreadfully from hay fever and it's imperative that I wear it outdoors while the pollen is as heavy as this,' he said.

'I quite understand, please come in,' said Pam.

'What extraordinary animals—are they a type of cat?' he asked, as he entered the house and removed his hat and mask.

'Yes, they're Siamese,' said Pam, 'I really must apologise for their behaviour; they're always very proprietorial, but this time they've really overstepped the mark.'

As soon as I heard Pam talking to him in a friendly manner, I stopped my banshee wails and the fur on my back gradually returned to normal, while a few vigorous flicks restored my tail. Ziggy, however, remained upstairs, determined not to confront the strange apparition.

I went into the garden where I remained until I saw the visitor's car leaving, and then I hurried upstairs to look for Ziggy. I found him in Laura's room under her bed, the dark brown of the valance round the base camouflaged him from a casual glance by anyone else—but I could distinguish him clearly. Pushing my nose underneath I said:

'You can come out now Ziggy, he's gone, but I'm afraid that Pam is rather angry with us. Let's go down together and say how sorry we are for our bad behaviour.'

'What an odd looking man,' said Ziggy as he slid out from under the bed on his back—propelling himself by thrusting his hind legs against the underside of the base. 'He scared me stiff when I saw him framed in the doorway.'

'He was obviously a friend,' I exclaimed, 'so we must make amends.'

'Pam looked very cross; do you think she'll smack me?'

I knew Pam wouldn't, but it would do Ziggy no harm to think that she might.

'Well, if we go and apologise right now, before she has to come and find us, she'll probably forgive us,' I told him as we went quickly down the stairs to find her.

We located her in her study, writing a letter, and leaped on to her desk so that our faces were level with hers. We nudged her with our noses, while keeping our eyes downcast to convey abject penitence.

'I should think so, too,' she said. 'Your behaviour was dreadful and I was very ashamed of you. However, I do appreciate how you felt because my reaction when I saw him was much the same, although I managed to control myself. I don't think he'll come again for some time—he was still shaking when he left.'

Ziggy and I repeated our apology and then wandered into the garden to snuff the warm heavily perfumed air of the summer evening, leaving her in peace to finish her letter.

A month or so later, we heard Pam telephoning a travel agent to book another flight to Mallorca and, since we knew that something was afoot, we decided that we would monitor all calls until we knew what was happening. Ziggy was on duty by the telephone when Pam arranged for us to be boarded at the cattery the following week. Despite our protests, which included refusing to speak to her and turning our backs if she attempted to pamper us, we were eventually put in the car and taken to the cattery.

Throughout the journey, we screamed at the top of our voices; Graham issued one or two threats concerning what would happen if we did not shut up, but it made no difference and the journey continued noisily until we reached the familiar gates. He stopped the car and turned to look at us—both now quietly sitting with lowered eyelids. We were going to miss Pam and Graham and we had behaved very badly by giving them such an unpleasant journey with our bansheeing. In order to atone for this, I opened my eyes and gazed adoringly at Graham; Ziggy followed my example and actually managed to purr for Pam—even though we were both miserable at the thought of our impending confinement.

Whether by accident or design, we found ourselves in the same austere pen we had occupied on our previous visit. There was no one about, so I used what was left of my vocal chords to let it be known that we had arrived.

'Hello, hello, is anyone there?'

'Who's making that ghastly din?' said a feline voice from the neighbouring shed. 'There's absolutely no peace these days; don't make so much noise or you'll start the dogs barking.'

'Dogs, dogs!' I cried. 'Surely there are no dogs here.'

'Oh yes there are,' said the voice.

'The last time we were here there were no dogs,' I remarked.

'Well there are now and, when a car comes up the drive, they usually make a deafening row. If one of them begins to bark at night, they all follow suit—it's terrible.'

'How awful—we don't like dogs.'

'Who's we?' asked the voice, as its owner appeared through the cat-flap and I was able to observe the occupant of the next pen for the first time. He was a beautiful tom with a sleek, well-groomed coat, which was the colour of rich marmalade and exquisitely marked.

'Good afternoon, I'm Tia Maria and this is my son Ziggy.'

'How do you do,' he replied. 'I gather from what you said that this is not your first time here. I'm sorry if I was a little brusque but the barking of the wretched dogs is driving me mad. By the way, my name is Ginger—my family hadn't much imagination.'

'We didn't hear anything when we arrived—the dogs must have been sleeping.'

'How long are you staying?' he enquired.

'Just a week this time; our family has gone to Spain.'

'How exciting for them; mine are at home because a new baby has just arrived. They're frightened that I'm going to sit on it and smother it so they've sent me here for a fortnight while they get themselves organised.'

'Perhaps you're in the best place. I've heard that the whole house is disrupted by the arrival of a baby and they cry all the time, not like kittens.' I ventured. 'Ziggy come and say hello to Ginger.'

Ziggy, his eyes watering from the smell of disinfectant, sauntered over.

'Good afternoon,' he said. 'I'm not usually a miserable cat, but I do hate it here and these fumes really upset me; I must be allergic to them, but for my mother's sake I'm trying to be brave.'

'How old are you?' asked Ginger.

'In human terms I'm just over two, but in cat years I'm a teenager.' Ziggy replied.

'That may explain it then, youngsters take longer to become accustomed to strong odours. You'll notice that neither your mother nor I are affected but, on the other hand, you may be allergic. Hopefully you'll build up some resistance in a few days.' He was a very diplomatic cat!

Nobody was visible in the pen on the other side, so we spent some time talking to Ginger who told us his life story.

When he was only a few weeks old, he had been taken to a pet shop to be sold. It was a frightening experience to be in the proximity of dozens of other cats and dogs and the sanitary arrangements left much to be desired. He had been a sickly youth and was embarrassed when people looked at him through the shop window making disparaging remarks about his scraggy appearance.

Nobody was interested in buying such an ugly kitten and, as the weeks went by, he became increasingly neurotic—starting to spit at anyone who tried to handle him. Everything changed when a girl aged about twelve came into the shop and saw him.

'That's the one I want,' she said to her mother. 'He looks so forlorn and unloved but I'm sure I could make him happy.'

Her mother wrinkled her nose in distaste and pointed to a black kitten playing with its tail.

'Wouldn't you rather have that lovely black one over there?'

'No I want this one; I shall call him Ginger.'

With that, she bent down, picked Ginger up and held him in her arms.

'You poor thing,' she said. 'Don't worry, I'll look after you and I know that we'll be great friends. Come on let's go home.'

Ginger was so surprised that someone had spoken kindly to him that he completely forgot to swear and instead snuggled into the girl's arms. She was as good as her word and had looked after him tenderly for nine years.

When her baby arrived, however, it usurped him and took priority in her affections; her main concern was its safety and, while it was so small, she regarded Ginger as a potential hazard.

We were expressing our sympathy to Ginger when there was a gasp from the pen on the other side of us and I turned to see Sapphire staring at us in amazement. She was as beautiful as ever but had put on a little weight. Running up to the netting dividing our pens, she exclaimed:

'Tia, how wonderful to see you! I can't believe it; what a coincidence that we're here at the same time again. I was feeling so miserable at the thought of being alone for a week, but now I'll even enjoy it! My family has gone abroad again; they now have a holiday home in Mallorca. Is Ziggy with you?'

'Sapphire, how marvellous! What a lovely surprise to see you. Yes, Ziggy is over there talking to Ginger.'

'Fine,' she whispered, 'because I wanted to speak to you alone for a moment. I've some news for you—you'll never guess what's happened. Soon after I last saw you, I was sent off to another cattery to meet a most gorgeous blue-point and I am now expecting his kittens. In the pen next to mine, there was a magnificent seal-point male who looked so like Ziggy that I thought he must be his father; I approached him and asked whether he was called Ben. He was astounded to discover that I knew his name and enquired if we had met before. I told him that we had a mutual friend called Tia and he sat down abruptly, becoming quite misty-eyed at the mention of your name.'

'How wonderful!' I exclaimed. 'Did you tell him about Ziggy?'

'Yes, I informed him that he was the father of a fine son and that you were both fit and happy in your new home in the country, although there had been a problem during the birth of your kittens which made it impossible for you to have another litter. He plied me with questions, wanting to know every detail I knew about you both. When I left; he made me promise that if I ever met you again, I would give you his love and assure you that you were constantly in his thoughts.'

My heart pounded and I could barely control my voice as I asked:

'Do you think that he still loves me?'

'Of course he does; he talked about you incessantly and was mortified when he realised that he would probably never see you again.'

That night I was able to tell Ziggy that Sapphire had met his father and how proud he was of his son. As I drifted off to sleep, I thought of Ben and my dreams were filled with pleasant memories of our brief time together.

With such good companions, the time passed quickly and it did not seem long before Pam and Graham came to take us home. Their arrival coincided with that of

Sapphire's family and they all chatted while waiting in the office for the three of us to be brought from our pens.

As we were carried in, I overheard Graham remark:

'I believe we were on the same flight from Palma yesterday.'

'Why yes, I thought I'd seen you before. Our name is Wilson—Ken and Joan. So these are your Siamese?'

'Yes, they've been here for a week this time while we were looking at property in Mallorca. My name is Graham and this is my wife Pam,' Graham replied.

'We have a holiday home near the northern town of Puerto Pollença and we try and get over there as often as we can. Sapphire is now pregnant so we'll not be going again for some months—we wouldn't dream of leaving her until the kittens are a few weeks old,' said Joan.

There was much discussion about the island while our accounts were settled and we were secured in our baskets; addresses were exchanged and the two families agreed to keep in touch. As I said farewell to Sapphire, I made her promise to convey my love to Ben if she ever went back to his cattery.

It was good to arrive home. Ziggy did his usual laps round the lawn leaping high into the air and performing somersaults until he was totally exhausted. When the excitement had abated, we all went into the house and sat down together as it was obvious that Pam and Graham had something they wanted to tell us. We waited expectantly, listening intently.

'We find that we like Mallorca so much that we've decided to live there,' said Graham.

What did this mean? Would we be sent to the cattery permanently or would they find another home for us?

Instinctively Ziggy and I moved closer together and we started to tremble.

'It's all right,' said Pam. 'You'll both come with us; we wouldn't dream of leaving you behind. You'll love Mallorca; the climate is warmer than here and there's sunshine for most of the year. We've bought some land at the top of a mountain where there's practically no traffic, just miles and miles of open countryside for you to explore. Our new house should be completed in about nine months, so we could be there for Christmas.'

The opportunity to explore a vast area in comparative safety and glorious sunshine seemed like paradise and sounded almost too good to be true—I could hardly wait!

# 10. Family Misfortunes

As he grew older, Ziggy became more independent and spent an increasing amount of time on his own, although we still spent much of the day together. One crisp winter morning, when there had been an overnight powdering of snow, I was walking ahead of him as we patrolled the grounds and suddenly realised that he was no longer behind me; I turned and saw his paw-prints leading down the drive. The trail stopped at the closed gate but, by peering through the rails, I could see that it continued on the other side. The heavy five-bar gate had presented no problem to Ziggy who had scaled it and raced across the busy road. I had repeatedly warned him never to do this and was dismayed to find that he had succumbed to temptation. He had disobeyed me and when he eventually returned I gave him a strong reprimand; instructing him never to cause me so much anxiety by wandering over the road again.

'Don't worry, Mum, I'm all right. I must have a bit of adventure; I love being with you and we have fun together but I need to go off on my own occasionally to explore the neighbouring territory,' he said reassuringly.

His growing wanderlust worried me and I recalled what Pam had told us about Mallorca. A house in a secluded position at the top of a mountain seemed to be the ideal place for him to indulge in his desire to roam.

One day he returned triumphantly from an expedition, his legs straddling a whole chicken, which he had been forced to drag along the ground because it was too heavy for him to carry. It was plucked, dressed and ready for the oven so I knew that he must have stolen it from the kitchen of one of our neighbours, but there was no way of knowing which. Although Siamese have a natural tendency to thieve, I approved when Pam spurned his gravel-coated offering and gave him a thorough scolding when he deposited it at her feet.

I observed all this but kept silent. Pam couldn't resist smiling at Ziggy's audacity but she was obviously worried about what would happen when the loss was discovered. I could see from her expression that she was thinking that your Siamese was certain to let you down in front of your neighbours, and I wondered what excuse she could offer if someone suddenly appeared on the doorstep complaining about the theft of a chicken. However, nobody ever mentioned the matter and she never discovered whose dinner Ziggy had stolen.

Ziggy became quite famous for his escapades. One neighbour told Pam that she heard a knock on her door and, when she opened it, Ziggy rode into the house with his front paws on the knocker and his back legs on the weather-bar, like a postillion at the rear of a landau. Once inside, he dropped off, shot up the stairs and hid under a bed as she followed in close pursuit. Fortunately for him, she had left the front door wide open and, while she hunted for him in another bedroom, he was able to streak downstairs and make his escape. Ziggy was certainly enjoying life but I worried that one-day he would overstep the mark.

At about this time Pam was obviously unwell; she had difficulty climbing the stairs and would sometimes need to lie down on her bed for a few minutes to recover her breath. On these occasions, we would sit like sentinels— one on either side of her—until she felt better. Eventually we learned that she had a heart problem and would have to go into hospital for a major operation; all plans for selling the house and moving to Mallorca had to be postponed. When she returned from hospital, Ziggy and I were never far from her side; initially on her bed and later on a lounger in the garden, listening as she told us more about the island.

She soon recuperated enough to stroll round the grounds in the afternoon and we escorted her, playing hide and seek with one another when she stopped to inspect some snowdrops pushing their fresh green shoots through the soil, and then racing to catch up with her when she moved to another plant.

These walks usually took us along the herbaceous border where Ziggy would make a dive into the catnip and perform his curious antics as he succumbed to its hallucinatory influence. Sometimes its effects had not completely worn off by the time he rejoined us and he would be jealous and aggressive; first attempting to take a nip at Pam's ankles, if he thought she was not paying enough attention to him, and then chasing me—trying to bite my bottom.

At this point Pam would come to my rescue, sweeping me into her arms and shouting at Ziggy: 'Stop that—you'll hurt her.' She would then carry me back to the house

while Ziggy gradually recovered his senses and was genuinely sorry for his boisterous behaviour.

'Mum, forgive me. I didn't mean to be so rough; I get carried away by that stuff and it's always so exciting to chase something.'

'Yes, I know,' I replied, 'but it doesn't always have to be your mother!'

As winter gave way to spring, Pam recovered sufficiently for the family to resume preparations for the move to Mallorca. Some decorating had to be done before the house could be offered for sale and we decided to be as helpful as we could, marching from room to room offering advice. Unfortunately, we didn't always notice which area had been painted and our bodies often radiated a strong smell of turpentine, which had been used to clean paint from our fur after we brushed against a newly decorated doorway. Being fastidious cats, we would spend hours licking one another in an effort to rid ourselves of the offensive odour.

Even during the mundane task of decorating, Ziggy managed to survive another potentially dangerous incident. We had fallen asleep on one of the beds while Pam painted a window frame and, as she raised the lower sash, I woke and saw a bird flying towards the open window. Ziggy, who always dozed with one ear cocked, heard its startled squawk as it spotted us lying on the bed and, completely forgetting that we were on the first floor, sprang straight through the open window, sailing downwards with all limbs extended like a sky diver.

Pam and I peered down and watched as he landed with a thud on the lawn below but, despite having fallen about twelve feet, he was completely unhurt and merely shook himself as he walked away—trying to give the impression that his impromptu flight had been intentional.

Ziggy was not the only one who did stupid things. Siamese are naturally inquisitive and I am no different from my peers. One day, Ziggy had braved the weather, which was unusually cold for the time of year, and had gone off alone on a hunting expedition. It was far too cold for me outside, so I walked around inside the house inspecting everything and taking some exercise at the same time. Pam and Graham were relaxing in the lounge so I decided to investigate the bedrooms. On the landing, I spotted a metal ladder, leading up to a square hatch in the ceiling that I had never seen open before. I had to know what was up there and curiosity overcame my normal caution.

I found that I was able to climb the ladder with ease, gripping the rungs with my front paws and feeling for them with my hind legs as I progressed upwards.

It was very dark at the top because there were no windows in the roof but, as my eyes became accustomed to the dim light, I could just make out a large open space with a boarded floor on which were stored a wide variety of interesting objects. I jumped from the ladder and started to explore an unfamiliar world where everything was covered in dust and cobwebs. I rummaged into stacks of old gramophone records, exercise books from the girls' school days, assorted toys and chipped china ornaments; there were also two broken chairs, a doll's pram, a tricycle, several pictures with broken glass, some battered suitcases with a hint of green mould on their leather trimmings and dozens of exciting cardboard boxes.

I was absorbed in inspecting these fascinating items when I suddenly became aware that a small grey cat was watching me from the shadows and I felt my fur begin to stand on end. How dare it come into our house and how long had it been there? I sprang at it, gripped it firmly round the neck and simultaneously kicked at it with my hind legs. I expected some sort of retaliation, but there was none; it was only when pieces of imitation fur and stuffing fell to the floor in front of me, that I realised I had wasted a great deal of energy fighting what had once been a very realistic toy.

Nearby there was a doll's cot, complete with bedclothes, a pillow and even a miniature eiderdown. It looked very inviting and I climbed in, luxuriating in the feel of its woollen blankets against my fur; it had obviously belonged to the girls when they were very young. I had not seen it before because they were already grown up by the time Ziggy and I arrived, but downstairs there were photographs of them as children and I could imagine them playing with the cot, putting their dolls to bed. They could not have known that one day a Siamese rummaging through the loft would find it and settle down for a catnap!

I awoke with a start, not knowing how long I had been sleeping, and walked to the top of the ladder to peer down at the landing below. The house was silent but I could see a dim light shining up from the hall through the stairwell. The ladder, which had been so easy to climb, proved impossible to descend. It had been simple enough for me to jump from it on to the solid floor of the loft, but the narrow top rung offered too small a platform for me to reverse the process. Realising that I was too high to jump down, I let out my loudest banshee. This had no effect whatsoever—Pam and Graham were unable to hear me because they were watching television, but I continued calling from time to time and eventually heard a patter of feet below me as Ziggy came bounding along the landing.

'Mum, where are you?' he cried.

'I'm up here!'

'Where, where, I can't see you.'

'Can you see the ladder?'

'Yes, I see it.'

'I'm at the top looking down at you from the square hole.'

'Why don't you climb down?' he asked.

'I can't, every time I try, I feel I'm going to fall.'

'Hang on, I'll get help.'

With that, he disappeared from my view and a few minutes later, I heard Graham calling.

'T-i-a, where are you?'

My banshee soon told him where I was and he looked up.

'What on earth are you doing up there? Oh dear, I suppose it's my fault for leaving the ladder down, but I really didn't expect either of you to be stupid enough to go into the loft. Don't move, I'm coming.'

He climbed up and took me in his arms; I could feel my heart thumping rapidly as he held me close and I nuzzled his neck as he carried me down. When we were safely on the landing, he pushed the ladder back into the loft and closed the trap door.

'Where was she?' asked Pam as we entered the lounge.

'Would you believe, in the loft. She must have been there for hours—she's absolutely filthy.'

At that point, I began to sneeze and I felt in need of a good wash. Ziggy helped me, using his large tongue to clean my head and neck while I attended to my paws. The relief of once again being with the family and not marooned in the loft was too much and I found that I was very tired after my adventure. Soon both of us were fast asleep, curled up together in a chair close to the fire.

The house was eventually ready for sale and an estate agent, a large brash man, came to take the particulars. We objected to his disrespectful attitude towards Pam and felt he needed taking down a peg, because we could not allow anyone to treat her in such an insolent manner. There was one certain way to get the better of him and that involved Ziggy playing his favourite trick.

I hid behind an armchair and watched while Ziggy scaled a mahogany tallboy and then climbed gingerly onto the top of the open door between the hall and the sitting room, where he crouched and awaited his opportunity. His patience was rewarded when we heard the agent approaching and, as he came through the doorway, Ziggy dropped straight down on top of him. The agent was so startled when Ziggy landed on his back that he let out a shriek and collapsed to his knees—toppling forward until he was prostrate on the carpet with Ziggy straddling his neck as he lay motionless. His papers, which he had been carrying as if they were of national importance, were scattered everywhere.

Pam heard the strangled screech and ran to see what had happened. She lifted Ziggy, gently unhooking his claws from the man's suit as she did so, while he struggled to his feet and turned to face her:

'Your cat nearly killed me,' he whined.

'He was only being playful, and you don't seem to be hurt,' replied Pam. 'Anyway, it's his party piece, which he isn't able to perform very often because all our friends know about it and take care when walking through open doorways. I suggest you get on with taking the details as quickly as you can—he probably won't do it again today!'

As he measured the rooms, we became entangled in his tape almost tripping him up; while he inspected the grounds we entertained him with an acrobatic display, leaping into the air, racing round the lawn, scrambling up a tree only to drop down in front of him, and generally distracting him so much that he had to measure everything twice.

Before departing, he turned to Pam saying: 'I trust you'll keep those cats under control when prospective purchasers are viewing the property; I'm sure that I can find a buyer for your house, but only if those animals keep well out of the way.'

Naturally, we did no such thing. Our tactics when people came to look round the house were simple but invariably effective. As they made their way from room to room, we used our knowledge of the geography of the house to ensure that whichever door they opened revealed at least one Siamese cat awakening from deep slumber. When they inspected the dining room, they would see us asleep on the chairs. As they left, we would race along the terrace and into the lounge, where we would stretch ourselves out on the sofa and begin to rub our eyes as they entered from the hall.

Similarly, a layout of interconnecting bedrooms, bathrooms and dressing rooms on the upper floor enabled us to give the impression that a least a dozen cats were permanently in residence.

Nearly every potential buyer asked: 'How many cats do you have?' and seemed very unconvinced when told that there were only two. We, of course, enjoyed every moment of this activity.

Suddenly, the house was withdrawn from the market, not because of our roguish behaviour but because it was Graham's turn to need urgent surgery. I fretted for his return from hospital and spent most of my time dozing on his chair in the study while Ziggy continued his normal pursuits.

Claire came to stay with Pam while Graham was away. The day after his operation, they were allowed to visit him, and before they set off together Pam called us to come in from the garden. I heard her and responded immediately but Ziggy was nowhere to be found; although Pam went on calling for some time, he still did not come. Eventually, after waiting as long as they could, the two of them left, leaving me safely in the house with the cat-flap locked and Ziggy shut outside.

About half an hour later, I spotted Ziggy through the study window; he was at the far end of the lawn near the gate and was dragging himself very slowly back to the house, using only his front legs, with his body stretched out behind him. Obviously in great pain, he was crying continuously and making very slow progress; he had to keep stopping to rest because the exertion was too much for him. When he reached the cat-flap and found it locked, I spoke to him from inside.

'What's happened, why are you unable to walk? Pam has gone to the hospital to see Graham but she called you for a long time and had to leave when you didn't come.'

'Mum, I've been hit by a car. I'm sorry, I know you told me never to cross the road but I looked both ways and didn't see the car coming—it must have been going very fast. I'm in agony and I can't stand up; I'll lie down by the yew hedge until Pam returns,' he sobbed as he spoke.

He dragged himself the few yards to the grassy bank by the yew hedge, moaning with pain as he moved. I was beside myself with anxiety and wished that I could reach him to comfort him. Pacing up and down, I prayed that Pam and Claire would return quickly. After what seemed an eternity, I heard their car coming up the drive and went to the front door to meet them as they came into the house, screaming frantically for them to follow me.

'Tia, what's the matter? Has Ziggy come back?'

I ran to the garden door with Pam following close behind me. As she unlocked it and stepped outside, she saw Ziggy lying by the hedge and rushed straight to him— only then realising that he had not responded with his usual greeting and continued to lie inertly. She picked him up gently and carried him into the house, while I followed them looking up anxiously.

'What's happened, where have you been?' she asked him. 'I didn't like leaving you outside but I had to go to Graham.' When she put him down, he started crying piteously and both of us rushed to comfort him. I began to lick his head but then he fainted and Pam, realising that he was very badly hurt, telephoned the vet who agreed to see him immediately.

'Look after Tia while I take Ziggy,' she said to Claire. When she had gone Claire picked me up and put me on her lap to stroke me but, even though I loved her, I was so distraught with anxiety for Ziggy that I couldn't settle and jumped down to pace the floor again.

About an hour later, Pam returned to the house alone and I listened anxiously as she told Claire that the vet had examined Ziggy and found that his leg was broken. He intended to anaesthetise him and set it, keeping him at the surgery overnight to recover. None of us liked the idea of Ziggy remaining there all night but there was no alternative. I was still frantic with worry because I was convinced that it was more serious than a broken leg.

Only ten minutes after Pam had returned, the vet telephoned and told her that there had been complications; Ziggy had been more extensively injured internally than he thought and, despite his strenuous attempts to save him, Ziggy had died while under the anaesthetic. Pam was beside herself with grief; I have never heard a human being cry with such choking sobs. Claire tried to comfort her as best she could, while I crept away to my basket to attempt to come to terms with what had happened to my beloved son.

# 11. In the Air

Everything changed after Ziggy died and I wondered how we were going to live without him. I still expected to hear him come bounding in through the cat-flap joyously announcing his arrival with his deep-throated voice calling:

'Mum, where are you?'

I had never considered that he would die before me and found it very difficult to adjust to the loss of his love and companionship. I could not bear to walk near the herbaceous border because it still contained the nests in the catnip where he succumbed to the hallucinatory effects of its pungent smell. Every part of the house and garden seemed to haunt me with memories of him; the basket where we used to curl up together in the warmth of the utility room, the old cashmere sweaters on Pam's desk where he had loved to lie and watch her work, the tree from which he had been shaken into the old sheet and the terrace where Graham had rescued him from the squirrel.

Pam and I had never been particularly close because I had always favoured Graham, while she was totally besotted with her beloved Ziggy, but our mutual loss drew us closer. We spent much more time together and I tried not to brood over the tragedy, directing all my thoughts towards our future life overseas, but I was overcome with emotion whenever memories came flooding back to me and sought the refuge of my basket until I recovered.

Graham returned from hospital but had to undergo several weeks of radiotherapy to ensure that his problem would not recur; nevertheless, it was possible to put the house back on the market and seriously plan our move to Spain.

I was eager to avoid doing anything that might deter a potential buyer, unlike previously when the whole business of selling the house had seemed like a huge game and Ziggy and I played tricks on the agent and prospective buyers. When people came to view the house, I would slink off to my basket and stay there until I heard them depart. These inspections became more frequent; one couple in particular returned several times, staying longer on each occasion and I was not surprised to hear that they had bought the house.

Activity then became frantic as preparations were made for the impending move. The house in Mallorca was much smaller than the one in which we were living and would be unable to accommodate its entire contents. The furniture was categorised into three groups; the best-loved items were set aside to go to Spain, some of the remainder went to a flat in London to provide a base for the girls, the rest was sent to an auction room in the local town. A start was made on packing china, glass and other fragile items and thirty tea chests were soon filled ready for transport.

The house looked very bare after the pictures had been removed from the walls and the ornaments were all wrapped and packed. Fortunately, the new owner had agreed to buy the fitted carpets and curtains so we were still quite comfortable, although it no longer felt like home.

Pam and Graham had to comply with many formalities relating to the importation of their possessions into Spain and strict regulations also applied to domestic pets; these included a medical examination by a UK government approved vet the day before travelling to Spain in order to obtain the necessary certificate of health.

After the removal date had been confirmed and seats were booked for the flight, with special permission for me to travel with Pam and Graham in the club class section of the aircraft, the complex machine on which Graham was having his treatment broke down. Although arrangements were eventually made to transfer him to one of the few other similar units in the area, the inevitable delay meant that he would have to remain behind when Pam and I left for Spain. Fortunately, our good friends Eric and Rita were free to accompany us and help with the paperwork that had to be completed before the furniture could be unloaded in Mallorca.

Removal day dawned and we heard the large furniture van manoeuvring into position outside the front door while we were having breakfast. From a window on the stairs, I had an excellent view of the enormous van, which would travel across France and Spain and then by ferry to Mallorca. Despite its size, I wondered how all the furniture and tea chests, not to mention the garden equipment, would be accommodated. I knew the ride-on lawnmower and the roller and the leaf-sweeper would not be going with us because Graham had said that it would be impossible to have a lawn on our rocky site.

Before they started work, the men sat in the kitchen and Pam made them a cup of tea while she cleared the breakfast dishes. They didn't want anything to eat but they all lit cigarettes and Pam's face expressed her disapproval—she hated people smoking in the house, particularly in the kitchen, but she said nothing. Graham and I thought it wise to leave the scene and wandered outside to make sure that everything had been labelled and left in an accessible position for the men.

At last, they were ready to start! They worked hard, sweating profusely since it was a very hot summer's day; shifting furniture was heavy work and they needed numerous cups of tea to quench their thirst. I constantly monitored progress, running up and down the ramp that led into the van, inspecting each new addition to the load and ensuring that my favourite basket was not overlooked.

It was evening before everything was safely on board for the long journey and I had just entered the van to satisfy myself that my basket was there, carefully wrapped in polythene, when I heard the creak of the tailboard being raised, followed by sharp bangs as the fastenings were secured and padlocked. Shortly afterwards, I sensed the throb of the powerful engine and felt the van start to move down the drive. I was terrified because I had heard Graham remark earlier that the journey would take five days and the van would not be opened until it arrived at Customs in Mallorca.

Would they realise that I was trapped in the van before it reached the open road? I started to howl but nobody could hear me above the noise of the engine. When the van halted for the gate to be opened, I heard furious hammering on one of the side panels and Graham shouting at the top of his voice. The ignition was switched off and I took advantage of the ensuing silence to give vent to my loudest banshee. The padlocks were quickly removed and, as the doors were opened, I rushed to Graham who picked me up and turned to the men to thank them as he put me over his shoulder to carry me back to the house.

'Tia, what in the world were you doing? Do you realise that you could have been incarcerated in that van for at least five days? I can't even bear to think about it.' All the time he was talking, he was holding me tighter—we were both horrified at what could have happened. I was still shivering from fright as he put me down inside the empty house and I took refuge in a corner—had it not gone, I would have curled up in my basket which I had very nearly accompanied all the way to Mallorca.

Some friends had kindly invited the three of us to stay that night—knowing that we would be without furniture. Pam and I were scheduled to leave for Mallorca in the morning but Graham was staying with them until his treatment was completed. We were given a warm welcome on arrival at their house but I was taken straight to our bedroom. This was necessary because Smudge, their large black and white female cat, was not nearly so hospitable; in fact, she was positively hostile towards any other animal entering her domain.

When Pam and Graham went down for dinner, I was shut upstairs and it was not long before Smudge scented my presence. I heard her sniffing at the door and then scratching at it furiously, screeching at me and threatening to tear me limb from limb once she got her claws into me. If only she had paused for a moment in her tirade, I could have assured her that I would be leaving first thing in the morning. She was still muttering vile oaths when her owner came up after dinner and removed her to the kitchen—where she continued to protest for an hour or more until exhaustion finally overcame her.

Eric and Rita arrived early the following day. I greeted Rita warmly when she entered the bedroom where I was still confined to avoid the risk of my coming face to face with Smudge, who had started her wailing again. Rita picked me up and hugged me; I nuzzled her and purred loudly because I had loved her from the moment we first met in the boutique.

Pam and I said good-bye and Graham helped us into the car as we prepared to set off on our journey to the airport. Pam held me on her lap in the back but, on arrival, I was put into a large IATA approved plastic container to comply with airline regulations. Once inside the terminal we reported to the Palma check-in where Pam presented her ticket, explaining that she had brought the Siamese cat that was to travel with her in the cabin.

By this time, I was feeling bored and let out a banshee or two to inform the world of the fact. The girl at the check-in froze in horror, her fingers that had been expertly tapping the keys to issue Pam's boarding card went completely rigid and her mouth dropped open. Eventually she recovered her voice.

'All animals must travel in the hold,' she stated very emphatically.

'Oh no,' retorted Pam, 'I chose this airline because it allows one animal to travel in the cabin.'

'I don't have any notification about that; stay here while I check.'

Having kept us waiting for quite a time she returned grim-faced.

'It seems to be in order—put the cat on the scales.'

Pam complied, but on seeing the large IATA box the girl said triumphantly:

'You can't take that into the cabin because it's well outside the specified dimensions for cabin luggage, so the cat will have to go in the hold.'

'No,' said Pam, 'I have specifically arranged for her to travel with me.'

'Then you must get a small cardboard travelling box for the animal—Lufthansa have some.'

'I'm not going anywhere—you must get it.'

Pam sounded authoritative but I could tell by the slight tremble in her voice that she was close to tears. Fortunately, Eric intervened at this point and told the girl why Pam should not be subjected to any stress. This transformed her and she shot off like a rocket to collect the box. When she returned, I was transferred to it and the empty plastic container was labelled to go into the hold.

I was somewhat cramped in my new box but remained quiet while Pam carried me into the departure lounge where I could hear garbled announcements on the loudspeakers; each preceded by an unusual ding-dong that fascinated me. Once the movement stopped, I knew that Pam had placed the box on the seat beside her and I decided that the time had come for me to see something of my surroundings. I was nearly suffocated by the smell of new cardboard and in desperate need of a good stretch; moreover, my only vision was through some small ventilation holes.

My prison was shaped like a little house with a peaked roof; it opened at the ridge where two cardboard handles served the dual-function of enabling it to be carried and holding it shut. Initially, Pam sat with one hand firmly gripping the handles but, after a while, she became absorbed in conversation with Rita and I sensed that she had slightly relaxed her hold. Knowing the moment had come to strike, I thrust a paw upwards and easily separated the roof, quickly pushing my head through the resulting gap. Pam reacted instantly, using her free hand to press my head downwards until I was forced to recover my paw and sink back to the bottom of the container. We repeated this cycle at intervals but Pam's countermove was always just too quick for me to escape.

Eventually, I felt the box being lifted as the long walk to the plane commenced and I crouched with an eye pressed against one of the ventilation holes, determined not to miss a single detail of this new and interesting world. Although I knew that Pam was carrying the container very carefully, I was still thrown from side to side as she walked to the aircraft. We boarded the plane and Pam placed the box on the seat next to hers but I had to remain incarcerated until we were airborne.

The noise of hand-luggage being stowed in the overhead lockers was followed by a commotion because a throng of late arrivals were pushing and shoving their way down the aisle of the aircraft—their duty-free bottles of spirits clinking against one another in their plastic bags.

Before long, everyone was seated; I sensed that we were moving and soon heard the engines scream as we took off. When the noise had subsided to a steady drone, Pam opened the box and held my lead firmly as I padded from edge to edge of the two empty seats beside her, stretching first my front legs and then the hind ones. After giving my tail a couple of good flicks, I yawned and sat with it wrapped neatly across my front paws gazing up at her.

'That's right Tia, settle down, you'll be more comfortable now,' said Pam as she stroked my head and I purred in response.

For a time, I looked out of the window but there was nothing to see except endless clouds. I wondered what the rest of cabin was like but, from where I was sitting, I could see nothing except the backs of the seats in front of us and some people sitting on the other side of the aisle. The best vantage point would be from the top of my seat—so I hopped up. That was much better; through some open curtains, I could see Eric and Rita sitting further back in the cabin, and the airhostesses bustling up and down the aisle serving pre-lunch drinks.

Eventually, I concentrated all of my attention on an old lady in the seat directly behind us who was methodically knitting while she read a book. I was mesmerised by the ball of wool jerking around as she clicked her needles and failed to realise that I had been staring at her intently for some minutes. She must have felt my gaze because she suddenly looked up and saw me. I expected her to launch into the customary torrent of admiration with which strangers usually greet me and was totally unprepared for her violent reaction. Instead of smiling at me she shrank back into her seat and screamed in terror—how was I to know that she disliked all cats intensely and Siamese in particular?

Pam was oblivious to what was happening until she heard the scream and an airhostess appeared at her side.

'Please remove your cat from the back of the seat because she's frightening the lady behind you.'

'She's a very gentle cat—I can't believe she's frightening anyone and she's on her lead.' said Pam in surprise. However, she reached up and pulled me down beside her, stroking me to calm my shattered nerves. 'What a silly woman; I hope she didn't upset you too much Tia. They'll be serving lunch soon and I'm sure there'll be something nice for you.'

She was right. When the tray arrived, I immediately detected the smell of smoked salmon, which I adore, and Pam insisted that I should eat as much as I wanted; in fact, I devoured her entire portion and then scrounged some contributions from the couple across the aisle who were Siamese friendly and had been watching me with fascination. The airhostess filled a bowl with water for me and, after this excellent lunch, I washed, curled up into a tight ball with my paws over my ears and slept on the seat beside Pam for the remainder of the journey to Palma.

After leaving the plane, we waited in the luggage hall to collect the cases and my large plastic travelling box. Pam had discarded the cardboard contraption and carried me in her arms. When the carousel started to move there were several curious objects among the usual travelling bags and folded push-chairs; these included a pink china washbasin crudely wrapped in brown paper, and the entire exhaust system for a Volkswagen tied into an untidy bundle with coarse string. I gazed with sympathy at four miserable dogs who peered anxiously out of the gates of their containers as they were carried round on the moving belt like prizes in a quiz show. They had travelled in the hold of the aircraft and were still circulating slowly, forlornly awaiting their owners, long after we had recovered our luggage. I was thankful that I had been able to travel in the cabin and not as a piece of baggage.

Pam had obtained all the necessary documents needed for my entry into Spain but she had been warned that I might have to spend the night at the airport if the official vet was not available. Her Spanish was limited and she had written out several Spanish phrases to use if we were taken to the vet's office. However, the Customs officer barely glanced at my papers and handed them back to her immediately.

'*Pase, pase,*' he said, waving her through.

'*Gracias,*' said Pam, quickening her pace before he changed his mind.

The air was warm as we emerged from the terminal and I could feel the heat rising from the concrete during our short walk to the car that Eric had hired. I sat on Pam's lap and had my first glimpse of Mallorca as we drove out of the airport and along the motorway to Palma. Numerous windmills lined the road; some restored, others with broken or missing sails like discarded toys. It was not an ideal introduction to the island because my sensitive nose was assaulted by the smells of brewing, sewage disposal and the manufacture of bottled gas before we cleared the industrial area near the airport and drove alongside the sea into Palma.

Hundreds of luxury yachts were clustered in the large marina in front of the curved promenade and the opposite side was lined with hotels and restaurants. I was so absorbed that I completely forgot my dislike of travelling by car and remained silent. Not long after we left the lights of the city behind us, we turned off the motorway and drove for about twenty minutes to the small town of Calviá; then we climbed steeply on a winding road through thickly wooded hills until we entered a gateway leading to a small courtyard.

As Eric unpacked the car, I was carried into the house and taken to the bedroom I would be sharing with Pam. I had expected the smell of new wood and paint, but this was quite an old house and the furnishings were completely strange. The room was comfortable enough but I was tired of being confined and eager to sample the freedom that had attracted me to Mallorca. However, it was now dark and the shutters were closed, so I would have to wait until morning before I could see exactly where we were.

That night I could not get to sleep but sat like a sphinx on the twin bed alongside Pam, fixing her with an inscrutable stare that she found rather disconcerting. Every time she opened her eyes, she saw me gazing at her, motionless but reproachful, as I tried to overcome my disappointment.

In the morning, everything looked different—the sun was shining and I was taken out on my lead for a breath of fresh air. It was heaven to stretch my legs and inspect the new surroundings but my pleasure was short-lived because I was suddenly bundled back into the house and heard the car drive off. Pam, Eric and Rita did not return until quite late and, from their conversation that evening, I gathered that they had been busy all day in Palma attending to the myriad of details relating to immigration.

This boring existence continued for several days and I began to feel really miserable, screaming at intervals to vent my vexation. Where was our furniture and where was my basket? I had watched everything being loaded into the van, but I was rapidly giving up hope of ever seeing our possessions again. Then, one morning, Pam packed her clothes and we went out to the car where Eric and Rita were waiting.

'Now Tia, we are going to our new home.'

Within three minutes we had reached the top of the hill and stopped in front of a bright white house. Pam carried me inside and put me down on a marble floor, which felt cold beneath my paws. The first thing I noticed was the smell of fresh paint and then I recognised our furniture and knew that at last we had arrived at our final destination.

I inspected every room and soon worked out the layout. In the kitchen, I found my basket awaiting me and could not resist getting in and lying down. It was a tremendous relief to experience its familiar comfort after such a traumatic week.

A day or so later, Eric and Rita left for their return flight to England. I was sorry to see them go as Rita always had time to talk to me and hug me, while Eric knew just how to end a stroke with a gentle pull of the tail.

That evening Graham was due to join us and Pam transmitted her excitement to me as we eagerly awaited his arrival. It had been a very warm day and the air was still balmy outside on the terrace while we listened for the sound of his taxi. When we saw its lights coming up the hill, we rushed simultaneously to the front door to welcome him.

I gazed adoringly up at him as he embraced Pam and noted that he was looking fit and well after his treatment. He picked me up and kissed my neck, while stroking my body, and when he set me down I wrapped myself around his legs, pressing myself against him to show my pleasure at seeing him again. He produced a bottle of champagne and we all sat together on the terrace in the moonlight, gazing down at the lights on the coast far below us as we savoured our new lifestyle.

In this totally new environment, I felt much calmer than at any time since Ziggy's death and found that I could think about him without too much heartache by concentrating on the good times we had enjoyed. Similarly, although I often thought about Ben, I had long since abandoned any hope of seeing him again and was content just to remember the brief time we had together.

I slept very soundly that night, curled up snugly in my own comfortable basket.

# 12. Over the Wall

The following morning, I awoke at the sound of the kitchen door being opened and saw Graham's smiling face looking down at me.

'Hello Tia,' he said. 'Did you sleep well?'

I purred loudly as I got out of my basket and had a good stretch. This complex routine entails sliding my front legs alternately along the floor as far as they will go and simultaneously raising the rear half of my back with my tail erect, then standing with stiff front legs and extending my hind legs in turn as far back as possible, finishing with a slight shake of each rear paw. Graham waited for me to complete this ritual before lifting me up and holding me close as he stroked my head.

'I thought we would take a look outside,' he said. 'It was dark when I arrived last night and I haven't seen the house since it was finished. Anyway you might like to have a wander around in the fresh air.'

With that, he opened the door to the back terrace and we descended some steps to a broad gravel walk. I noticed an old stone wall a few yards away, which was obviously the boundary of our property, and decided to walk along the top. It led me into the grounds of the neighbouring house where I saw two people eating breakfast on their terrace.

In order to get a better look, I crawled forward under some bushes with my belly scraping the ground and my tail stretched out behind me. The earth was dry beneath my paws and the dead leaves crackled even though I moved stealthily. As I moved closer and crouched down to make myself more comfortable, I could see the couple clearly and heard them talking and laughing quite loudly. Unfortunately, during a pause in their conversation, the weight of my body snapped a brittle twig with a sharp crack and they looked up.

'What was that?' asked the woman peering in my direction as she rose from the table and walked towards the bush beneath which I was hiding. She was middle-aged with a rounded figure and grey hair and, although she had a kind face, I decided not to stay if she came any nearer. She failed to spot me and turned back to rejoin the man I assumed to be her husband.

'I couldn't see anything George—it must have been a bird.'

'No, a bird wouldn't make a noise as loud as that, it must have been something heavier—pass me some more toast please, Carmen.'

He was far more interested in his breakfast than any possible intruder and I watched him take the toast and spread it thickly with marmalade. This reminded me that I had abandoned Graham before breakfast, so I broke cover and bounded towards the wall, the brittle twigs snapping loudly under my paws like Christmas crackers at a party. Behind me, I could hear excited voices as the couple reacted to my hurried departure.

'George, it was a beautiful cat,' said Carmen.

'It must belong to our new neighbours,' he replied.

Graham was waiting for me by the wall and remonstrated with me when I returned.

'Don't go too far until you get your bearings, Tia. It would be a tragedy if you got lost after having come such a long way.'

He was right and I decided to stay close to the house until I had familiarised myself with my new surroundings. How Ziggy would have loved Mallorca! The air was clean, warm and filled with fascinating scents, many of them unfamiliar to me. I could easily identify the distinctive smell of warm pine needles, but it was some time before I became accustomed to the strong, medicinal aroma of the lentisk bushes. Some of the flowers were new to me but I recognised lavender and rosemary when I found them growing wild in the garden.

A few days after we arrived, our neighbours came to visit us; Pam and Graham invited them to have a drink on the terrace so that we could all become acquainted. Carmen obviously adored cats; I allowed her to hold me on her lap and she stroked me continuously while murmuring to me affectionately in Spanish.

Pam introduced me: 'This is Tia Maria, she's a chocolate-point Siamese.'

'She's very beautiful—we saw her darting out of our grounds the other day while we were having breakfast but she wouldn't come anywhere near us,' said Carmen.

'No, she's very nervous of strangers but she'll be better when she gets to know you,' Graham replied.

Carmen was obviously fascinated by me and offered to look after me if Pam and Graham ever wanted to go away. I liked Carmen but was horrified at the thought of being left so soon after we had arrived—forsaking Carmen's knee, I rushed over to Graham and draped myself around his shoulders.

'Hey, what's the matter with you?' he enquired. In response, I pushed my nose into his neck and butted his ear while he stroked me soothingly.

As the days lengthened, I heard an extraordinary noise with increasing frequency. At first, I thought it was electricity flowing through some overhead wires, but sometimes it stopped and then started again almost under my nose. Eventually, I traced it to what looked like a huge grasshopper—called a *cigarra* in Mallorca. These insects live in the pine trees that surround us, and their buzzing grows to a crescendo during July and August when they call to one another from sunrise until sunset.

I spent many happy hours wandering through the mountainous countryside, fascinated by the native fauna. I could not resist chasing birds, rabbits and mice; sometimes catching one and carrying it home triumphantly—proudly depositing it at Graham's feet. On such occasions, he was very diplomatic and thanked me profusely before disposing of it surreptitiously.

Because there were sheep grazing on the land behind the house, I wore a special collar to prevent their ticks burying themselves into my skin and sucking my blood.

During one of my hunting expeditions, I came across a large hare and immediately attacked it; we fought hard for some time and I managed to wound it—but my front paw became entangled in my tick collar and I had to let it escape. Limping home on three legs over rocky terrain was very difficult; I was exhausted by the time I reached the house and collapsed in front of Pam and Graham, who were enjoying a quiet drink on the terrace.

'What's happened to Tia—she's covered in blood?' Pam cried—her voice betraying her concern.

'I don't know, I think she must have been hit by a car,' replied Graham as he jumped up.

'Is she badly hurt?'

Graham felt me all over and removed the offending collar to release my foot.

'She seems to be all right, but we can't really tell until we've washed away the blood.'

Pam went for a bowl of warm water and a sponge and I had to suffer the indignity of standing with my hind legs in the water while she washed my underbelly.

'Ugh! She must have had a fight with something, but what animal has so much blood?' Pam cried.

'Possibly a hare,' observed Graham. 'Fortunately none of the blood is hers—I can't find a cut anywhere.'

When I was reasonably clean, although still a little wet, I lay in the sun on one of the loungers and washed myself until I was satisfied that my fur was almost back to normal.

The tick collar was never replaced but every time I came back from one of my outings, I was subjected to a thorough inspection. Any tick that was discovered on my body was soaked in alcohol until inebriated—whereupon it released its grip and could be extracted with a pair of tweezers.

Being an inquisitive Siamese, I could not resist exploring the neighbouring gardens. I liked to visit George and Carmen's grounds and would usually wander along the wall and just drop in. There was a terrace on one side of their house and I liked to slink along it, swaying my hips and looking as seductive as possible.

'T-i-a, T-i-a,' Carmen would call hoping that I would stop and speak to her, but I was far too intent on exploring to be distracted.

One evening, I had skirted around their house and was on my way home when I noticed an open door underneath their terrace. This was too much of a temptation and I ventured into a low-ceilinged cellar filled with interesting piles of sacking, wood, tiles, fertiliser, bags of cement, garden tools and a variety of old household items. I was so absorbed in rummaging through everything, that I failed to hear footsteps approaching—only realising what was happening when I heard the metal door to the cellar slam and a key being turned in the lock.

I froze with horror. There had been a shaft of light through the doorway, but now the whole area was plunged into darkness with only a few small beams piercing some ventilation holes in the upper part of the door. I cursed myself for stupidly ignoring my natural wariness of strange places and was frightened by being shut in with no means of escape.

My loudest banshee produced no response and I sat shivering in the dank atmosphere, wondering how long it would be before I was released. I hoped that Pam and Graham would soon miss me and come looking for me; but lately I had been wandering off for much longer periods and they might not think my absence unusual. Feeling very miserable, I crouched down on a pile of sacks, which were reasonably comfortable but offended my sensitive nose.

I awoke from a fitful sleep to see chinks of sunlight around the edge of the door, so I knew that it must be morning and that I had been there all night. As there was no sound of movement above, I realised that George and

Carmen must have locked up the house and returned to their apartment in Palma.

Siamese are supposed to be more intelligent than other cats, but I had managed to get myself shut in a dark basement with no food or water. I wondered why Pam and Graham had not looked for me and then realised that they could not hear me crying; the cellar was a long way from the road and the locked gates would prevent them searching near my dungeon.

The possibility that George and Carmen might be gone for several days filled me with panic and I started to calculate how long I could hold out. I had already scratched determinedly at the door and butted it with my head, but it would not budge and I knew that there was no point in wasting any more effort on an attempt to escape.

Several hours later, I heard Graham calling me but his voice faded in the wind. I tried in vain to attract his attention with a loud banshee but could only manage a faint croak. There was no more I could do, so I settled dejectedly on the sack—wishing with all my heart that I was back in my basket with a plate of food and a bowl of water beside me.

Suddenly, I heard footsteps approaching and the key being turned in the lock. As the door opened, I gathered all my strength and bolted out, pushing aside an astonished George who gave a startled shout and almost fell over backwards as I raced off home. I expected a warm welcome from Pam and Graham but instead they were furious with me.

'Where the devil have you been?' shouted Graham as I attempted to settle on his knee. 'We've been out of our minds with worry and spent half the night searching all over the mountain for you. Don't ever stay out like that again.'

At that point, the telephone rang and Pam went to answer it. When she returned she sat down with a sigh.

'That was George. Apparently, he shut the door to their cellar just before they went to Palma last night and locked Tia inside, not knowing that she was in there. It was only this morning, when he unlocked the door and she shot out, that he realised what had happened. He's most dreadfully sorry and insists that we have keys to the gate and the cellar in case she's ever shut in again.'

'What a silly girl!' the tone of Graham's voice changed. 'You must be absolutely starving. Come and have something to eat.'

How right he was! I had not eaten anything since breakfast the day before and was glad that George had telephoned, because they might otherwise have assumed that I had been catching and eating mice all night, instead of being shut in the ghastly cellar.

We went to the kitchen together and I was soon tucking into my favourite meal of chicken and gulping down some fresh water—it was wonderful to be back with my family.

Graham left me to eat in peace and joined Pam who had made some coffee and was relaxing on the terrace—they were deep in conversation by the time I joined them and settled down to wash myself. I felt in need of a full-scale bath and chose one of the comfortable loungers, on which I could roll over easily in order to wash the other side. Even my claws needed attention, because they had been damaged when I tried to scratch the door open. I soon dealt with them by biting them close to my paw and pulling off the outer sheaths to reveal wicked new points.

Very sharp claws can be more of a nuisance than an asset, as I learned to my cost through a humiliating experience. I was sitting on the back terrace, watching Pam hanging out some washing, when a blackbird flew just in front of me and perched on the line. This was an opportunity I could not resist and I sprang towards the washing line, climbing up one of the wet towels until the bird was only a few inches from my mouth. To my horror, I then found that my claws had become firmly hooked into the material and I was unable to extricate them. As the startled bird flew off to a branch, its droppings fell with a splat on top of my head and down the clean towel.

The worst thing that can happen to any Siamese is loss of dignity and I knew that I looked very stupid, suspended in mid-air, swaying gently in the breeze and anointed with bird droppings. Fortunately, Pam noticed my predicament and, while suppressing a laugh to spare me further embarrassment, she lifted me with one hand, gently freed each claw with the other and then took me in for a wash.

'Those claws of yours are far too long; I'll go and fetch the nail clippers so that you'll be more comfortable,' said Pam.

When she returned carrying the clippers, I viewed them with considerable alarm and we had quite a tussle before she found that she could pin me down with one arm and use her free hand to clip my claws.

I must admit that I now appreciate the points being removed periodically, to prevent them getting caught in my blanket or the doormat that I scratch every morning as part of my exercise routine—although I still hate the sound as my claws are snipped. However, Pam never cuts my hind claws as the vet has told her that I might need them to protect myself if I am attacked.

I had already grown to love Mallorca—there were so many interesting things to see, even on my own doorstep, and the weather was marvellous. It is rare for a Siamese to feel too warm but the garden could become uncomfortably hot; fortunately the house always remained beautifully cool and I was able to spread myself out on the marble floor to combat the heat.

Pam and Graham had arranged for a swimming pool to be constructed and it was soon ready for use. I had never seen one before and gazed in fascination as the two of them swam up and down. Deep water does not appeal to me and I am always very careful not to get too close to the edge. I usually sit in the shade of an oleander a few feet away on the terrace, with my paws tucked under me as I watch them enjoying themselves.

On hot summer nights, Pam and Graham frequently have a midnight swim. The lights on the terrace illuminate only part of the garden, leaving exciting patches of darkness where I can hear scuttling noises in the dry earth. While they swim, I slink down the steps leading from the terrace and amuse myself by observing every movement of the nocturnal creatures who are completely unaware that a Siamese is lurking nearby. Sometimes I become so engrossed that I fail to hear my name being called when it is time for bed.

Early one morning, I found that frogs had invaded the pool terrace. Several large plant pots were arranged neatly around the edge of the pool and, during very hot weather, their saucers were kept filled with water. Some tadpoles thrived there and turned into frogs overnight. What fun! I found that if I placed a paw gently in the middle of a frog's back it would jump just like a tiddly-wink. There were dozens of them and I played this game for some time, chasing after them until I became bored and decided to see what was going on inside the house. I had assumed responsibility for supervising the day-to-day running of our new establishment and was fully convinced that my constant attention was essential to ensure that everything went smoothly.

'Ah, there you are Tia! Been for a walk round the terrace? I thought I saw you a few minutes ago,' said Graham, as I entered and rubbed myself against him until he picked me up.

'What have you been doing? You've a very mischievous look on your face—come on you had better show me.'

With that, he put me down and followed me as I led him to the pool terrace. Not a frog in sight! Where could they have gone? I ran from one end of the terrace to the other searching frantically—but there was no trace of them.

# 13. A Visit from the Girls

The girls were coming! This was their first visit to our new home and I could not wait to see them again; growing more and more excited as preparations were made for their arrival. After Pam and Graham had set off for the airport to collect them, I waited impatiently in the house.

When I heard the car return, I went to the front door to welcome them, and soon recognised the sound of their familiar voices as they commented on the house and the fabulous view. When the door opened, I rushed out—squinting in the brilliant sunshine.

'Tia, Tia,' they both chorused as I leaped towards them. 'How are you, do you like it here?'

After they had both picked me up and kissed me repeatedly, I was handed to Pam and they followed their father who was struggling into the house carrying their suitcases.

'Make yourselves comfortable outside on the terrace,' said Pam as she headed for the kitchen to make some tea. She reappeared a few minutes later carrying the tray and joined the others who were laughing and joking. Laura lifted me on to her lap, stroking my head and tickling my beard, as the family exchanged news of mutual friends and recent events.

## A Visit from the Girls

I thought I should devote some time to Claire and jumped on to her lounger, walking slowly up her body until I could nuzzle her face. A moment or two later, she began to sneeze violently and her eyes started to water as she hastily blew her nose. This startled me and I dropped down on to the terrace to wait until the sneezing had stopped. After it had abated, I climbed on to her again but was quickly rebuffed; this was strange behaviour from someone who was normally so affectionate and I tried to settle on her one more time—only to be rejected again.

Feeling miserable, I crept to the other side of the terrace, away from the group, and started to wash myself as nonchalantly as I could, in order to work out what to do next. The build-up to their visit and the excitement of their arrival had evaporated; I could not believe that I had offended Claire and concluded that perhaps she was just tired after her long journey.

My spirits were fully restored, however, when Claire blew her nose loudly, apologised for the noise, and added:

'I'm afraid I have hay fever—I seem to be allergic to Mrs Tia Maria! I've not had much contact with cats recently and it may take me a few days to develop some resistance to her fur—I should be all right if I avoid stroking her for the moment. Poor Tia, she can't understand why I keep pushing her away.'

Now that she had explained her conduct, I felt better and rubbed myself around her legs as she got up and walked round the terrace, taking in deep breaths of fresh air, before returning to join in the family conversation.

'How beautiful it is here and how different from London! exclaimed Laura. 'The air is so pure and it's incredibly quiet.'

'Yes, we love it,' said Pam. 'When people think of Mallorca, they imagine crowded beaches and noisy bars but out here in the country it's exceptionally peaceful— we're very fortunate to have such magnificent views of the mountains and the coast.

'Tia also seems to like it here—how old is she now?' asked Claire.

'She's six—still a young cat,' was the reply.

'She looks younger now than she did in England. I suppose that's because she no longer has to worry about Ziggy. Do you remember all his escapades? He was an absolute rascal but such a gorgeous animal,' said Laura.

'Tia is quite capable of her own exploits and has disappeared once or twice, even managing to get herself shut in next door's cellar one night,' said Pam.

'Really, she always seems so sensible and dignified. She can be very frustrating at times though; I remember once, when I was in a hurry, she continued to walk at her own pace in front of me. No way could I get past her while she sauntered along swaying her hips and carrying that long tail of hers just above the ground,' Claire recalled.

'Terrible cat,' said Pam affectionately as she ruffled my fur and stroked my head.

Curled up on the end of her lounger, I listened to their chatter and occasionally opened one eye to gaze at them. I wasn't worried about Claire any longer, now that I knew that she still loved me.

We had dinner on the terrace, but went inside when the air became cooler. As the family continued to catch up with their news, I managed to stay away from Claire— who was still blowing her nose and wiping her streaming eyes. The hours passed quickly as the girls questioned their parents about their new life in Mallorca; it was well after midnight when everyone decided it was time to retire for the night, after such an exciting day. What the girls didn't know was that I was waiting for a sign of movement so that I could commence my nightly ritual.

In order to postpone going to bed, I had adopted the habit of hiding behind the furniture until Pam or Graham found me, then I would race round the room, leaping over the chairs, until I was eventually caught. Purring loudly, I would be carried to the kitchen to be incarcerated for the night and, as the door closed, I would let out my loudest banshee.

That night was no exception and, when they rose to their feet, I jumped down immediately and hid under the table.

'I thought she was asleep, what on earth is she doing?' asked Laura.

'She doesn't want to go to bed; we go through this performance every night but she's very happy once she's settled,' replied Graham.

The girls watched in amazement as both parents got down on hands and knees to try to capture me; it was a lovely game but eventually I had to give in and was carried off. They were saying goodnight to their parents as I emitted my first banshee.

'What on earth was that! I've never heard her make so much noise,' exclaimed Laura.

'Don't worry—there'll be two or three more and then there'll be silence,' explained Pam. 'She's just letting us know that she can still hear us talking and that it's time for us to go to bed.'

'Strange, she never did that in England.'

'You'll find that she does a lot of things that she never did in England,' was the reply.

The girls had come for a week and wanted to see the island, so I was shut in while they went off for the day. I was content to spend the time thinking and dreaming in the coolness of the house until the family returned—there was fire in the mid-day sun and the tiles on the terrace were so hot that they would have scorched my paws if I had walked over them.

I looked forward eagerly to the evening and would rush to meet them, as the sound of the car scrunching on the gravel heralded their homecoming. A moment or two later the girls would burst into the house crying:

'Tia, Tia, we're home!'

Since they both called together, I sometimes had difficulty in making myself heard and, on occasion, would have to resort to a banshee which would always stop them dead in their tracks.

'Ah! There you are—had a nice day?' one of them would enquire.

Had a nice day! What did they imagine I had been doing? I had given myself a bath and done my nails but that was about it. I had already explored every nook and cranny of the house so there was nothing left to do but snooze in my basket.

The girls obviously enjoyed exploring Mallorca and talked incessantly about each day's activities. By the end of the week, Pam and Graham had shown their daughters all the beauty spots that were within easy range of the house.

Graham groomed me daily in the shade of the north terrace with the aid of a toothcomb, removing large quantities of surplus fur, and followed up with a vigorous brushing that I loved; I would rub my nose against the brush to indicate that I wanted more. Being confined indoors every day, I was unable to stalk through the long dry grass and my fur remained free from pollen. In consequence, by the end of the week, Claire was able to stroke me occasionally without succumbing to one of her attacks of hay fever.

When it was time for the girls to pack for their homeward journey, I decided that they needed some help and climbed in and out of their suitcases several times to make sure everything was in order.

'Tia, come out of there and stop rummaging amongst my clothes; that's the third time you've tossed my tee-shirts on the floor!' cried Laura, absolutely exasperated. She scooped me up in her arms and gave me a kiss as she carried me to the door, closing it firmly behind me and saying: 'Now perhaps we can get the packing finished.'

Soon they were ready to depart and I felt sad that they were leaving. I wondered when I would see them again, Pam and Graham would be able to visit them in England but I had to remain in Spain. I could travel to other parts of the continent, but an archaic quarantine law meant that I would be isolated for six months if I set foot on British soil.

'Good-bye Tia, we'll think of you enjoying the sunshine while we're sheltering from the rain in London and we'll return as soon as we can,' they chorused as they got into the car.

The house would not be the same without everyone talking and laughing at the same time—it was already very quiet and they had only been gone five minutes. I went straight to my basket—always my place of refuge when I felt miserable. It contained a foam-filled cushion, cut to shape, which was covered by a fleecy blanket overlaid with a piece of white quilting—the remains of an old bedspread. I had several sets so that my bed could be changed every week to keep it fresh and clean. Sleep soon overcame me after I wriggled under the quilt, completely hidden and very comfortable.

Pam and Graham returned from the airport and I heard the kettle being filled for tea. I stretched as I climbed from my basket.

'Ah! There you are Tia, I didn't see you covered over like that. The girls will be in the air by now but they said they had a wonderful time and enjoyed seeing you again,' said Graham as Pam carried the tea through to the terrace and they settled on the loungers. I had a quick drink of water before I joined them.

Pam turned to Graham and remarked:

'It was lovely having the girls but I feel rather exhausted and it would be wonderful if we could have some help in the house. The people on the corner are moving to America and they have an excellent girl cleaning for them who may be prepared to work for us after they go. I've spoken to her and she seems interested, but she'd like to see the house before deciding.'

'That's fine—go ahead and ask her to come up.'

# *14. Gregoria*

And so it was that Gregoria came into our lives. She was young and married to a Mallorquín, although she herself was born on the Peninsula—no task was too much for her and she was always smiling. The whole house throbbed with activity on Fridays when she arrived; I formed the habit of hiding in the peace of the utility room if the weather was cold or taking a stroll down the mountainside on fine days—in order to escape the noise of the vacuum cleaner and the general bustle of housework.

After Gregoria had been coming to us regularly for six months, her visits suddenly ceased. For some weeks, I still anticipated the sound of her old Talbot rumbling up our drive on a Friday morning, but I eventually assumed that she would no longer be coming and was surprised when her somewhat battered car reappeared while I was patrolling the grounds after breakfast.

She entered the house carrying a large rush basket and placed it gently on the sofa, then went to the kitchen to start work. Pam and Graham were upstairs and I was alone in the *salón* so I advanced towards the unfamiliar object.

I had just placed my front paws on the edge of the sofa and was straining my neck to peer inside the basket, when I became aware of a smell that I vaguely remembered. It was the mixture of talcum powder and wool that Ziggy and I first encountered when we jumped into Susan's pram many years before. As nobody was around, I thought that I might settle in the comfortable interior and was about to leap up when Gregoria came back into the room and saw me.

'No Tia! No!' she shrieked as she rushed forward and lifted her new baby from the basket.

I ran out on to the terrace as Pam and Graham, who had not heard Gregoria arrive, came down to investigate the noise. I could hear them calming Gregoria and admiring her offspring, while I crouched behind the door.

'Graham, go and find Tia, she's probably upset,' said Pam as Gregoria settled the baby in its carrycot.

It only took a moment for Graham to find me cowering on the terrace—recovering from Gregoria's sudden outburst. He handed me to Pam who cuddled me and then took me over to the sofa.

'Look Tia, it's Gregoria's baby. Isn't she lovely! Gregoria has brought her today so that we can all see her. Don't disturb her; she needs to sleep the whole morning.'

Once I knew what was in the cot, I was no longer curious and, when the episode was repeated two years later, I was careful not to disturb Gregoria's second baby.

Gregoria was very fond of snails, which feature prominently on the menu in most Mallorquin restaurants as *caracoles en salsa*—or snails in sauce. They are usually cooked in olive oil flavoured with garlic, onions, tomatoes and parsley; a little diced ham may also be added to the mixture. In the gastronomic pecking order they equate approximately with the position occupied by frogs' legs in France, while wild mushrooms—known as *setas,* hold the same elevated status the French accord to truffles.

## A Visit from the Girls

Pam and I listened as Gregoria extolled the virtues of snails and explained how to cook them to perfection, but I could never contemplate eating one however it had been cooked, and I am still convinced that it could not possibly compare with a freshly caught mouse. I knew by the expression on Pam's face that no way would she ever eat snails and I doubted whether she shared my fondness for mice.

After overnight rain, Graham searched the garden on Friday mornings and usually came back with a few small snails for Gregoria, which he put into a plastic bag, tying the top to prevent their escape. He would hand this to her when she arrived and she always thanked him, but eventually she displayed her own prowess as a snail catcher. After Graham had presented her with his usual small collection, she asked if she could have a look around in case any more had emerged from their various hiding places; she was only away for a few minutes and returned with the bag half full. She can spot a snail if only a tiny part of its shell is visible and her eyesight must be nearly as good as mine.

One Saturday afternoon, while enjoying the sunshine on the porch, I was surprised to hear the distinctive sound of Gregoria's car coming up the road, because she had been with us only the day before. After parking alongside Pam's car, she emerged with a good-looking young man who was a stranger to me.

What followed was completely incomprehensible. The two of them attacked Pam's car and started to wreck it; removing the soft velvet-covered seats, the thick grey carpets and the headlamps. Many other bits and pieces were taken off and deposited in a pile on the drive. Then they turned their attention to Gregoria's car, which was a

*141*

similar model, though older and much more basic. When they took out its seats, I noticed that bits of stuffing were showing through cracks in the plastic covering, and the floor mats were little more than scraps of torn felt. Before long, a second pile of parts matched the first.

I watched with growing concern—Pam's car was old, but Graham had looked after it carefully and it was always clean and well polished. It was rapidly becoming a total wreck and I was powerless to prevent its destruction. I had just decided to go in search of Graham when he came out of the house and, ignoring the two gaunt-eyed cars in the driveway, greeted Gregoria warmly—shaking hands with the young man whom she introduced as her brother. Then the whole process was reversed with Graham assisting with the reconstruction, but this time all of the worn items went into Pam's car while Gregoria's began to look very much smarter than when it had arrived.

After Gregoria and her brother departed, I jumped through the open window of Pam's car to inspect the damage. It had been one of my favourite places for an afternoon nap, serving as a luxurious greenhouse where I was cushioned by the soft upholstery and protected from any cooling wind. Now it was a shambles, the seats were in tatters and wires projected where fittings had been quickly removed from the interior. Pam had always taken considerable pride in its appearance and I shuddered to think what she would say when she saw its tattered state.

It was Monday morning before Pam went out to her car and I watched with some trepidation, expecting her to cry out in astonishment, but she expressed no concern and drove off as if nothing had happened.

When she returned an hour or so later, driving a brand new Ford, I realised that our old Talbot had been replaced.

I waited until Pam had gone indoors and hopped in through the open window of the new car. It was blissful, even more comfortable than the old one, and I settled down to give myself a thorough groom—unfortunately this was during my moult and when I got up to leave I found that the black velour upholstery was covered with a generous deposit of my white fur.

Later, I heard Pam telling Graham that she had found it strange to drive her degraded car to the garage in order to collect her new one because everything felt different and she could barely see over the steering wheel. When she arrived, the salesman admired its shiny paintwork and observed that it seemed too good to go for scrap—but when he opened the door and saw the interior, his eyebrows shot up at the sight of the sagging seats, torn upholstery, tattered carpets and missing parts. He led her to her new purchase and commented:

'After your old one, this should feel like a Rolls-Royce!'

# 15. Sights & Sounds

In Mallorca, there are virtually only two seasons—summer and winter. In high summer, it can be uncomfortably hot, but usually it is pleasantly warm and I love the feel of the sun on my fur. Winters are generally mild and I can only remember one when it was so cold that we actually had snow. In England it would not have been remarkable but the Mallorquins found it enthralling; I sat on our wall watching as about fifty cars, all filled to capacity with excited families, drove past me on their way up the mountain to the open ground from which they could observe the full extent of the fall. There were many squeals of delight as children, who had never seen snow in their lives, made the most of the rare event.

On chilly evenings, we enjoy being together in front of a log fire; Pam and Graham either read or watch television but I seldom pay much attention to the screen. However, on one occasion, I looked up and saw two cats having a conversation regarding the merit of a particular cat food; one was ginger, the other was a grey tabby. I found the advertisement fascinating and craned my head forward to get a better look. Graham noticed my interest and recorded it for me, playing it back from time to time because he thought it would please me.

He would take me on his lap and stroke me saying: 'Watch this, Tia!'

I would purr loudly, as I twisted my head to gaze adoringly up at him, while he smiled down at me. He thought I was enjoying the commercial but, in fact, I was smiling and purring because I loved being on his lap—frankly, the advertisement had started to bore me stiff! Nevertheless, I still had to eat all the tins of cat food that had been bought in the misguided belief that it would please me.

I have grown up surrounded by the electronic marvels of television, radio and recorded sound. For most of the time, I ignore them, although I greatly enjoy dancing with Pam to a good rhythm. However, I am sometimes deceived by the fidelity of modern sound reproduction and two recent incidents fooled me completely.

The first was when Claire came to visit us with her new husband. She was working on an interesting project and the local radio station invited her to talk about it. I knew she had left the house to go to Palma, but I had no idea that she was making a live broadcast and was startled when I heard her speaking in the *salón*. I searched everywhere for her until I realised that her voice was coming from the hi-fi.

The second occasion was even more of a shock. Graham was struggling to improve his Spanish and I came into the room as he was conjugating irregular verbs. He paid no attention when I wailed several times and went on reciting, so I turned my back on him and left him to get on with it—completely unaware that he was recording a tape. When he played it back a few days later, I was dozing on the sofa and was astonished to hear a Siamese cat screaming loudly. I was about to dismiss the noise as a figment of my imagination when it called again, even more demandingly. My fur ridged along my back and I was fully prepared for battle before I realised, with some embarrassment, that it was my own voice protesting when he made the recording.

Graham mainly uses our video recorder to capture the British television broadcasts that we receive very clearly in Mallorca via satellite. His first VCR was a bulky affair that lived on a shelf under the TV; it lasted for many years but finally reached the end of its days and was replaced by a very smart new model—so compact that it was placed on top of a low cabinet close to the set.

I had no difficulty in jumping on top of the new recorder to inspect it. Once there, I found to my delight that it had some slots in the top, which had obviously been put there to warm my bottom as I sat washing myself, and I made full use of the facility.

There was one programme that Pam hated to miss and, as she was going to Palma, she set the timer on the recorder. Two hours later, while I was relaxing after a very thorough wash, it suddenly started to operate just beneath me with loud clicks and whirrs that made me race for cover, until I realised that it was harmless.

The recorder was one of my favourite spots until the machine developed a fault. The repair man was called and, on opening it up, found that it was full of my hair. I was definitely out of favour with Graham when he learned the cause of the problem and he reacted promptly by standing a potted plant on the top—thereafter it was definitely out of bounds, forcing me to find a new place to groom myself.

The heat of the house attracted a family of dormice—known in Majorca as *lirones*. They are pretty creatures with black-ringed eyes, a brown back, grey underbelly and a long tail ending in a tuft—but they have a vicious bite and can climb vertically up walls. They managed to penetrate a small terracotta ventilation brick, constructing a nest in the space between the ceiling and the roof—on most nights we could hear them scuttling overhead.

George warned Graham that they could cause short circuits by gnawing at the insulation on electric cables and he produced a trap in the form of a wire cage. Its hinged door slammed shut when anything started to nibble at some bait impaled on a hook. This proved so effective that Graham lost count after fifty dormice had been caught, transported unharmed, and released on the mountain—I thought that I recognised a few of them and suspected that they had returned only to be trapped again. Graham expected me to show some interest in the captives as they sat in the trap waiting to be taken away, but I pointedly ignored them since I am only excited by the thrill of the chase.

The trap was not selective and other animals foolish enough to be tempted by the bait also found themselves captured; these included two small rabbits, a large rat and a very fat hedgehog. The hedgehog presented Graham with a problem because it totally filled the trap and its spines acted like ratchets, allowing it to enter the cage but preventing its exit. Eventually, in order to release it, he had to separate the wires from the base of the wooden floor of the trap and open it up sufficiently for the hedgehog to drop out and walk away.

Graham only captured baby rabbits in his trap but I became adept at hunting them and frequently caught quite large ones. Initially, I used to consume them but my habits have changed as I have grown older and I no longer feel the urge to catch and kill all the wildlife in our vicinity. I have become more human than I would have believed possible when Ziggy and I went on hunting expeditions many years ago, and I now approve of Graham's method of capturing and transporting any animals that are unwelcome around the house.

Before our solid gates were installed, all creatures had free access to our garden and they came and went as they pleased, enjoying the plants and herbs—particularly the parsley, which one stray sheep demolished in a couple of quick mouthfuls. After the gates were fitted, the rabbits sharing our habitat were trapped and unable to escape— perhaps they no longer felt the need since I no longer presented a threat to them.

My interest was aroused, however, when I observed one rabbit continually visiting a clump of irises in the border. Curiosity overcame me and I nonchalantly strolled over to investigate; I was amazed to see five newborn rabbits huddled together in an indentation in the centre. Unfortunately, when the mother rabbit saw me poised over her family, she attacked me and managed to land a couple of vicious swipes across my face before I was able to retreat. Infection set in and we had to visit the vet in the village who immediately gave me a course of antibiotics.

On another occasion, the vet saved my life. One morning I was unable to use my litter tray and became totally exhausted after toing and froing for various attempts— becoming so weak that I could no longer stand up. Pam, in response to my cries, came in from the terrace where she had been watering the plants and discovered me spread out on the dining room carpet, moaning intermittently.

She immediately realised that I was desperately ill and picked up the telephone to call the vet, but her emotions got the better of her and she started to cry. I found myself willing her to stop weeping as she was very incoherent and I was certain that the vet was having difficulty in understanding what she was trying to say. At last, she put down the receiver and, still sobbing, disappeared from my line of vision; I knew that she had gone to fetch my travelling basket.

I will never know how she managed to drive with tears streaming down her face, nor will I ever forget hearing someone in the queue remark, as we were ushered quickly into the surgery:

'It's an emergency, the cat is dying.'

I lay on the table while the vet examined me and Pam anxiously asked him what was wrong.

'Let me look at her first and then I'll be able to tell you,' was his brusque reply.

He took my temperature and gave me three injections while I lay motionless—my anxiety matching Pam's.

'Bring her back this evening,' was all he would say.

We returned home and it seemed an eternity until it was time to visit the surgery again. The procedure was the same as before, although this time there was no queue for me to jump. I was given three more injections and Pam was told to return the following morning.

When we arrived the next day, the vet gave me yet more injections and explained that he had been very concerned about my condition, remarking that it was fortunate Pam had acted so quickly.

'Only last week I had a cat in a similar condition, but her owner delayed bringing her down for twenty-four hours and we lost her,' he said.

'Was Tia's temperature very high?' Pam enquired.

'On the contrary, it was too low. She had a blockage in her colon; the injections were to start things moving again and disperse the obstruction—possibly, she had eaten some dried grass. Bring her back in a week's time, but she should quickly recover now.'

He was right and I was soon healthy again but, while I was recovering, I stayed close to Pam and Graham so that I could enjoy being pampered.

Once I had regained my strength, I resumed my hunting expeditions on warm summer evenings and occasionally failed to return to the house before nightfall because I was completely absorbed in stalking nocturnal animals. This entailed waiting for hours crouched flat on my belly with my tail stretched out behind me—my body blending with the colour of the earth and rocks. I could hear Pam and Graham calling me to come in but, although reluctant to disobey them, I turned a deaf ear because the slightest movement would have aborted hours of patient waiting.

Sometimes I stayed out until long after they had retired for the night. When I returned, my only means of attracting their attention, so that I could enjoy the comfort of my basket, was to stand under their bedroom window and give a loud banshee. At this the shutters would fly open and Graham would shout angrily down to me:

'Tia, what time do you call this? Stay there and I'll come and let you in.'

The subsequent ritual was always the same—grim-faced, he would open the door without uttering another word and I would walk penitently towards the kitchen and slink into my basket, knowing there would be no supper for me that night.

# 16. Abducted

One Friday in summer, in order to evade the noise of Gregoria's cleaning activities, I went for a stroll in the cool air before the sun reached its zenith. Instead of walking through the neighbouring gardens, as was my usual custom, I decided to follow the road down the hill. It wound snake-like to the village several kilometres below and I sauntered down slowly, snuffing at the pungent smells of the indigenous plants growing along the verge. This was a fateful choice. As I wandered deep in thought enjoying the feeling of the sunshine on my back, I became aware of a car crawling slowly beside me, a window being wound down and then a voice entreating:

'Hey, pussy, pussy, come pussy!'

Pussy, pussy! Who did they think they were speaking to? I was no mere pussy; I was a thoroughbred Siamese! I walked on taking no notice, my nose tilted skywards as the car continued to crawl alongside. Without warning, it suddenly accelerated and swerved to a halt in front of me, forcing me to stop dead in my tracks. I was totally unprepared for what happened next and it is something I shall never forget. A woman flung open a door of the car and jumped out, grabbing hold of me before I had time to turn tail and run. She thrust me into a foul-smelling sack, which she pitched into the back of the car as she screamed at the driver:

'Step on it—I've got it!'

I struggled inside the sack but to no avail, the woman had knotted it tightly and there was no hope of escape; it was stiflingly hot and I could barely breathe. I had been dumped on the floor, which felt hard and uncomfortable; as the car swayed and sped on, I wondered where they were taking me and why? Pam and Graham would be appalled if they knew what had happened. Our area was considered safe because there was little traffic and few strangers ventured up the hill—apart from organised walking parties accompanied by guides.

Neither of my captors spoke a word after I was bundled into the car; we must have been travelling for about twenty minutes before it jolted along a bumpy track, slowed down and then skidded to an abrupt stop. Almost immediately, the door was wrenched open and I was carried unceremoniously in the sack for a short distance, and then dropped on to a hard surface.

'I think we're in luck,' said the woman as she opened the sack and hauled me out. 'This looks like a very valuable cat.'

'Don't know much about cats, particularly Siamese,' said her companion, who had driven the car. He eyed me as I sat crouched on the floor where I had been dumped; then, looking perplexed and scratching his head, he turned to the woman and said:

'What do we do next?'

While they were talking, I was able to survey my surroundings. The house appeared to be derelict and was sparsely furnished; curtains hung in tatters at a cobweb-covered window with a broken pane that had been replaced with cardboard. In the centre of the room, there were two rickety chairs and a table, which was littered with dirty plates, a half-empty bottle of milk and a stale-looking loaf of bread.

What was happening? Why had they brought me here? I had never encountered people like this before and they terrified me; my ears twitched nervously with fear but I was unable to cry for help because my throat was dry.

I scrutinised the man who was about fifty, with hair that was already thinning and a face that resembled one of the weasels I had seen in the mountains behind our house. He was not very tall, grossly overweight and pot-bellied from drinking too much beer. I wondered how the dilapidated chair on which he was sitting could take his weight, since he constantly shifted his position in an effort to get more comfortable on its inadequate seat.

Somehow, I managed to produce just enough saliva to moisten my dry throat, which enabled me to emit my first banshee.

'Blimey! What was that?'

They both looked in my direction and, having got their attention, I gave vent to another for good measure.

'I've never heard a cat make a noise like that before! Is it male or female?' asked the man.

'It's a female,' said the woman, who was as skinny as he was fat and had a snipy face framed by faded blond hair. 'We'll get a tidy sum for her—people living in that area aren't short of a bob or two; we must watch out for an ad in the paper—it shouldn't be long before her owner offers a reward.' As she spoke, a cigarette jerked up and down as it dangled between her mean lips.

She bent over me and the smell of her sweat was overpowering, making me heave with revulsion—her attempts to mask the odour with some cheap scent had failed dismally.

'We've always stolen dogs before, dogs is easy. I'm not so sure the nobs will pay up for a mog,' said the repulsive man.

'Course they will! Anyway, this is no mog, it's got real breeding and may be worth more than most dogs,' said his companion.

The next two days were interminable. I couldn't eat any of the cheap tinned food they put in front of me and I refused to drink the foul-smelling milk. It had not occurred to them that Siamese need water and I was dehydrated by the time they gave me some. My banshee had initially unnerved them but, as the days passed, it had grown weaker and no longer had any effect. My mouth and tongue were dry with fear, as well as lack of water, and I was unable to wash myself, which added to my misery, as I have always been a most fastidious cat.

By the third day, my captors were starting to show signs of concern.

'There's still no mention in the paper of a missing cat; we'd better act quickly now—otherwise she'll die on us,' said the man.

'Okay, we won't wait any longer for the owner to advertise,' said the woman. 'In this paper there's a breeder, only twenty kilometres away, advertising Siamese kittens—let's go there and see if she'll buy the cat.'

I was bundled into the car again, but this time I was thrown on to the back seat and covered with a rug, while the woman sat next to me holding me down—it would not do for the breeder to see me arriving in a sack!

We reached our destination and the couple hurried from the car into the office, the woman holding me firmly in her arms. I noticed that the buildings were similar to those of the cattery in England where Ziggy and I had been boarded.

The man marched straight up to a well-groomed woman wearing a white coat who was obviously in charge. Without any preliminaries, he asked in his grating voice:

'Are you interested in buying a female Siamese?'

The breeder, who had been busy at her desk, was startled by the sudden entry of two rough-looking people carrying an unkempt cat. She eyed them up and down as she answered:

'It's true I am looking for a Siamese to breed from but I would need to see her pedigree?

'We ain't got it with us,' said the man. 'If we strike a deal, we'll let you have it later.'

'Very well,' said the breeder. 'Just put her on the table.'

I gazed at her imploringly. She was tall with light brown hair and a kind face; her hands were soft and caressing as she stroked my back and felt my legs and tail. While doing this, she turned to the couple and said:

'She is very thin and her general condition is not good, but she's undoubtedly a fine animal. How old is she?'

They answered simultaneously:

'Two,' said the man.

'Four,' said the woman.

The breeder looked at them, but said nothing. She stroked my head and opened my mouth. It was then that I decided to play my trump card since she could not have failed to notice that I was nearer six. I rolled on my back to disclose the long scar on my stomach, at the same time giving her knowing looks and a sidelong glance towards my captors.

'Where did you get this cat?' she demanded. 'She's about six and has been spayed, so she's no use for breeding. If she were your cat, you would have known these elementary facts; I believe she's been stolen and I'm going to call the police.'

As she picked up the telephone, the man grabbed me from the table and the couple ran to their car, accelerating away without pausing to close its doors properly in their panic to escape.

The atmosphere in the car was tense as the man pressed his foot down hard on the accelerator, making the old banger hurtle along as fast as it would go. Eventually, he turned into the rutted drive, the car bounced to the end and pulled up sharply in front of the derelict house we had left only a few hours earlier.

'What do we do now?' enquired the woman.

'Oh, shut up! We've been duped by the cat; did you see the way she exposed her scar to the breeder? We might have got away with it if she hadn't done that and we would be quids in by now. What on earth made you go for a cat anyway—a dog would have been much easier to sell. We'll have to get rid of her!'

'No, we can't do that; it wasn't what we agreed. You promised we'd hold her to ransom or sell her to a breeder,' whined the woman.

'I know, but no one has advertised a missing Siamese; the breeder's on to us, and by now she'll have given our description to the police. We'll have to ditch her—I'm sick and tired of her constant wailing and you've never smoked so many cigarettes.

I listened to their conversation while crouching on the floor in a corner of the dirty room, fearing what was going to happen to me and distressed at the thought that I might never see Pam and Graham again. By now, they would be worried out of their minds by my disappearance and I doubted whether they could manage on their own without my constant supervision.

The woman then made a suggestion:

'Wouldn't it be better to take her fairly near to where we found her and release her. She'll at least have a chance of getting home. If we set off when it's getting dark, nobody will spot us.'

'I suppose you're right,' growled the man. 'Heaven knows she's given us enough trouble by refusing to eat and making that wretched din. She'll starve herself to death if we keep her any longer.'

I breathed a sigh of relief; I was sure that I could find my way home if they abandoned me in the vicinity. My sense of smell is extremely good and a few snuffs of the night air would almost certainly enable me to recognise something familiar.

That evening, just as dusk was falling, we piled into the car and once more bounced over the potholes in the dusty road. I could not see where we were going because, as before, the woman had put me on the back seat next to her and thrown the blanket over me—it was only one stage better than being in the sack!

We had been travelling for about twenty minutes when the car stopped. Removing the blanket, the woman said:

'Here you are, pussy, you're not far from home and I'm sure you're clever enough to find your own way back. You certainly fooled us!'

She opened the door and I tumbled out, making for the cover of some lentisk bushes as the car turned and careered back the way it had come. I didn't recognise my immediate surroundings, but I knew that I must head up the hill—after all, we lived at the top.

Stealthily, I moved upwards, taking care to retreat into the bushes whenever I heard a car coming, as I couldn't bear the thought of being captured again. It was hard going and I was exhausted because I had not eaten for several days, but I toiled on and on, only resting when I felt I could go no further.

There were no houses on that stretch of the road and by then it had grown dark, but I could dimly make out some lights in the distance and struggled towards them— ignoring the little mice and rabbits that scuttled unusually close to me, knowing that I was too tired to catch them.

Suddenly I caught a whiff of a familiar scent and knew exactly where I was; mustering up all my remaining energy, I prepared for the final climb to the safety of home.

It was not much further but could I make it? Would Pam and Graham be there? They had to be; I could not go on if I let myself think that they might be out for the evening. I staggered and fell, feeling that my legs could carry me no longer, but I made one last superhuman effort and crawled through a gap in the wire netting fence that surrounds our house. I just managed to reach the terrace door outside the *salón*, crying as loudly as I could, before I collapsed.

The door was flung open.

'She's here, she's here!' cried Pam to Graham. 'Oh Tia, we thought we'd never see you again!'

As she started to cry with relief, Graham came over to where I lay and carried me in.

'She's dreadfully thin and her paws are cut to ribbons. She obviously hasn't eaten for several days and she must have walked a very long way.'

I lay on the floor emitting feeble moans.

'We must give her some water,' said Pam as she picked me up and carried me gently to the kitchen. 'She ought to drink before she has anything to eat, but I've got some chicken in the fridge, which I'll give her later.'

She prepared my meal while I lapped at the water and then shook my head to remove any drips. This eased my dry throat and I was soon ready to tackle the chicken, struggling not to wolf it down too quickly.

'Just look at her, I've never seen her eat anything at such speed. I won't give her too much for the moment because her stomach isn't ready to digest it,' said Pam.

When I had finished, she carried me upstairs where I lay on their bed, with my throbbing paws hanging over the edge, unable to suppress my cries of relief at being back with my family.

'We'll take her down to the vet in the morning to make sure that she hasn't suffered any lasting damage, but I think she should stay up here with us tonight. She's obviously very disturbed and we can't leave her alone,' said Graham taking charge.

I gradually relaxed and fell into a deep untroubled sleep, safe in the knowledge that I was home at last.

# 17. Josephine

The next morning, after a little persuasion, I was put into my travelling basket for the short journey down to the vet. I was in euphoria at being home and refrained from making my usual protestations because Pam and Graham were still in shock—it would not take much for them to disintegrate. Earlier at breakfast, sitting in my favourite spot on the pine dresser where it caught the morning sun, I had watched Graham pour salt instead of sugar into his coffee; I remained silent because, had I spoken, he would have turned to look at me and gone on pouring. He discovered his mistake when he took his first sip and hastily tipped the contents of his cup down the sink before Pam noticed.

As we drove down the hill to the vet, we passed the spot where I had been dumped by my captors only a few hours earlier and I shivered as memories of that terrible experience came flooding back to me. The purpose-built surgery was attached to a beautiful house set high above the village of Calviá. The waiting room was almost full; several dogs, a marmalade cat, who reminded me of Ginger, a guinea pig and a bird were sitting patiently with their owners. After what seemed an eternity it was our turn.

The vet remembered me from my previous visits. His pretty, blonde wife was helping him that day; she smiled and made a tremendous fuss of me—definitely a cat person.

'Tia Maria, what a lovely name! Aren't you beautiful, but you're very thin!' she exclaimed.

Graham explained to them that I had been missing for five days and had only returned the night before in a very emotional state, adding:

'We've brought her down so that you can check her over. We've no idea where she's been, but she looked terrible when she crawled home last night; we think that she was stolen but somehow managed to escape.'

The vet took my temperature and then felt me all over; he had firm but gentle hands and I purred at his touch.

'You must be very relieved to have her back,' he said. 'I can't find anything wrong but I'll give her an antibiotic in case she has picked up something. Bring her down again in a few days and telephone me if you're at all worried about her.'

When we returned later that week, he seemed pleased that I had gained weight and gave me another injection—adding that he would like to see me later in the year for my annual protection against feline enteritis and other cat ailments. He also suggested that I should have an anti rabies injection, although it was not obligatory, just to be on the safe side.

During the next few weeks, I did not venture very far from the house, as I was still nervous after my traumatic experience. I spent a great deal of time with Pam and Graham and resumed my supervisory role, monitoring all internal activity and regularly patrolling the grounds;

occasionally catching the odd mouse that was impertinent enough to stray on to our territory.

When I recovered my nerve, and was ready to explore further afield, I wandered down the hill—but kept well clear of the road. As I picked my way carefully over the rocks, I sensed that I was being watched—although I could see nothing, my acute sense of smell told me that another cat was in the vicinity. This was confirmed when I pushed through a thick clump of broom and came almost face to face with another Siamese. I wondered whether it was male or female and if I should advance or maintain a safe distance. However, I need not have worried as a feminine voice greeted me politely:

'Hello, I'm Josephine! I've seen you once or twice before but I've always kept out of sight as I couldn't pluck up enough courage to speak to you.'

How marvellous to have found not only a friendly cat but also a Siamese!

'Hello, I'm Tia Maria. I live at the top of the hill.'

'Yes, I know. I live at the old *finca* further down the mountain. I saw you when you first arrived and stayed at the house opposite for almost a week; by hiding under the bushes, I could watch you unobserved while you were being taken for a walk on your lead. I sometimes heard you crying when you were left for the day and I felt sorry for you being shut in all alone. You look like a Siamese although your colouring is different from mine. You came over from England didn't you?'

'Yes, I'm an expatriate but that doesn't explain my colour. I'm a chocolate point and you're a seal point. Where were you born?'

'Why, here on Mallorca—so I'm a *siamésa mallorquina*. Now that we've met at last, I do hope we can be friends.'

'Yes, I hope so too. I have a lovely family but I do miss conversing with other cats. It was different when my son was alive and we chatted to one another all the time. Also, when the family went on holiday, we used to stay at a cattery and would spend many hours talking to some very pleasant cats.'

'You had a son?'

'Yes, but sadly Ziggy died following a road accident shortly before I left England. I had a daughter too, but I never really knew her as she went to another home when she was still tiny. My present family adopted Ziggy and me several years ago. Do you have a son or daughter, Josephine?'

'No, I was spayed when I was too young to have a family but I'm very happy. I belong to the son of the house and I sleep in his bed every night!'

'The only time that I've been allowed to sleep on the bed recently was when I returned after being stolen.'

'Stolen! How awful! You must tell me about it,' said Josephine. 'Let's sit down while we talk.'

We moved towards a patch of wild grass in the shade of a dry stone wall and settled ourselves comfortably while I recounted every detail of the terrible experience of my abduction. Josephine listened very sympathetically.

'How fortunate the breeder realised that you were stolen and frightened the thieves by telephoning the police— otherwise they might have held you captive much longer and not released you where you could find your own way home.'

'Yes,' I agreed, 'I love my home and would hate to live anywhere else. The couple who stole me intended to hold me to ransom; they failed because they were unable to make contact with my family. You've heard the rest, so let's talk about more pleasant things.'

Josephine agreed. I then told her about my life in England, my many adventures with Ziggy and my journey to the island. In return, she told me of her life in the old *finca* with her family.

'We have dogs guarding our house, which are normally kept on long chains, and it does worry me that one of them might attack me when they're allowed free for exercise,' said Josephine. 'However, I'm now more concerned about a group of feral cats that has moved into the neighbourhood—they might settle here permanently as the people living opposite have started to feed them. The leader of the gang is called Bruno but the others don't appear to have names. If they spot me, they chase me and I have to run for my life until I can scramble into our grounds through a break in the hedge. They never come very close to the house because of the dogs, so I'm safe once I'm home. Have you ever seen them?'

'No,' I replied, 'but I've heard strange voices on the other side of the wall at the end of our garden.'

'Well, just run if you spot them; the odds are stacked heavily against us with that mangy lot.'

'I'll certainly do as you suggest,' I assured her.

The sun had moved round while we were sitting curled up in the grass and we found that it was shining directly into our eyes. We were quite stiff from lying so long and, as we got up to ease our cramped muscles, I noticed that Josephine's stretch pattern was briefer and less elaborate than mine—it lacked the alternate extension of each leg and the finishing twitch of the tail.

'I really must be going now but I've enjoyed our first meeting,' I said, as we walked sedately side by side until our paths parted. 'I hope we'll be able to meet frequently; I don't think Pam and Graham have any plans to travel at the moment, so I should be free to come down again soon.'

'I'll look forward to that,' said Josephine. 'It's nice to have a friend nearby.'

She left me and descended to the *finca* while I turned to climb back up the mountain to our house, feeling pleased that I had found someone with whom I could exchange confidences.

Over a week later, I set off down the hill to find Josephine, although I did not know whether she would still be expecting me. It had been difficult to get away because some visitors had arrived and I was eager to observe everything that was happening in the house. There had been no rain for several weeks and the ground was very dry; the brittle grass scratched my paws as I clambered over the rocks and down the hill under cover of the bushes. I called Josephine's name to let her know I was on my way and was surprised when she answered from behind me almost immediately.

'I had just about given you up,' she said. 'It seems ages since I saw you.'

'Yes, I know, I'm sorry. We've been busy and I couldn't find time to get down here and back again. This is the first day that any of us have had to ourselves since some people arrived unexpectedly. They've gone now and Pam and Graham are spending the day restoring the house to normal.'

'My favourite nest is just a few yards away and, as the sun is very hot, we can lie there in the shade while we talk,' suggested Josephine—leading the way towards the seclusion of a dark green lentisk bush.

When we had settled, I told her all about my love for Ben and how heartbroken I was that I would never see him again.

'I've never had a husband, but your Ben certainly sounds absolutely charming,' she said.

We sat chatting side by side under the aromatic lentisk bush until it was almost dark.

'I must go,' I said. 'It's getting quite late and I ought to be back by now. There's a short cut over the wall of the new house that's being built near ours and, if I go that way, it will save time. We'll meet again just as soon as I can get away.'

With that, I set off and soon reached the building site. I had merely to leap on to the wall, drop down the other side and cross the road to enter our grounds—the wall was fairly high but I easily made the top. Unfortunately, I had projected myself with such force that I was unable to stop and overbalanced, falling into a squelchy mess on the other side.

The builders had been busy that day and had left a hose trickling into a pile of cement and sand; I landed with a plop right in the middle of the heap, covering my legs and underbelly with the porridge-like substance. It was difficult to escape because it sucked at me as I struggled to get free.

Although I finally managed to extricate myself, the glutinous mess adhered to my fur and, when I tried to clean it from one of my paws, I found that my tongue was coated with grit at the first lick. I needed help urgently because the cement was weighing me down and starting to set. Stumbling as quickly as I could up the steps leading to our pool terrace, I let out a warning banshee.

# Josephine

Pam and Graham were sitting on their loungers, enjoying a quiet drink at the end of a hectic day spent tidying up the house after the departure of their visitors.

'What's the matter with her?' Graham cried as he leapt up and ran towards me. 'Gracious, what has happened to you Tia! Quick Pam, get a bowl of water.'

Pam went for the water and, once more, I had to suffer the indignity of standing in a bowl while she sponged down my underbelly and legs. The wretched stuff was very persistent and it was some time before I was clean enough to be lifted from the bowl, free from any residual traces of cement.

Pam and Graham went inside to watch television but I stretched out in the last rays of the sun until my coat had dried; then I made my way to the kitchen where my supper and a long cool drink awaited me. After I had emptied the plate, I went into the *salón* to thank them. I nuzzled each of them in turn and then waited eagerly for the moment when the television was turned off and our nightly bedtime ritual commenced. I had to keep our game short that night as I was feeling very tired after my adventure with the mortar.

# 18. Mr Rubi

Our house is typically Mallorquin, with many gently sloping roofs; most of it is single storey but the main bedroom and bathroom are on an upper floor. The house is very still in the morning when I wake up; I only have to give a couple of cries for Graham to hear me and come downstairs to let me out of the kitchen, while he opens up the rest of the house. I accompany him when he returns upstairs to shower and dress and usually find the glazed doors of the bedroom open. They provide access to a balcony and I have found that I can jump on to the stone parapet and walk along to a point where it meets one of the lower roofs; from where I can make my way right around the house from roof to roof.

I like to linger over this circuit because it enables me to survey the whole of my territory and enjoy the incredible vista stretching beyond our garden and down the mountainside to the coast. On summer mornings, the ferry from Barcelona looks like a painted ship on a painted ocean as it makes its way to Palma, with the sun highlighting its white hull.

From the long roof at the back of the house, I can see the woodland that stretches up a valley behind the stone wall marking our boundary. Beyond the trees, two mountains dominate the scene; *Galatzo*, the giant, which looks like the peak in the Paramount Pictures symbol, and *Bauza* that has a rounded outline resembling an inverted pudding basin. I have prowled over most of the land within a few kilometres of the house but both of these imposing landmarks are beyond my range.

After snuffing the air to determine the weather prospects for the day, I continue my path over the roofs until I come to the one that joins the house just below Pam and Graham's bathroom window. I can easily reach the sill from the tiles and, if they are still bathing and dressing, a few good banshees result in the window being opened. A few minutes after I have been lifted from the sill and placed on the floor, I usually become bored and wander out again onto the balcony to commence another circuit.

Pam and Graham make their bed before going down for breakfast and I love to help by wriggling under the sheet and trying to dodge Graham's hand as he feels for me. I have no sooner been extracted than I repeat the performance as they replace their duvet, getting increasingly excited as I evade their attempts to catch me.

Unfortunately, they have sometimes finished dressing and gone downstairs by the time I return to the bathroom window and my demands to be let in go unheeded. When this happens, I am reluctantly forced to admit defeat and have to retrace my steps back to the balcony to re-enter their bedroom.

As I am still on the upper floor, I have to tackle the problem of descending the staircase. The only way I can manage on my own is by placing my front paws on a lower step and then hopping my rear legs down together, rather like a rabbit. It is undignified but effective, although I much prefer to be carried by Pam or Graham.

Another of my favourite games is to leave the house by the doors leading on to the front terrace, and then dash quickly round the garden to the glazed door of the kitchen while Pam and Graham are having breakfast. I stand on my hind legs, resting my front ones against the glass, peering at them and pleading to be let in. Graham gets up and opens the door and I deliberately brush against him to express my gratitude as I enter; but a moment or two later, I go out at the front and rush round again to gaze at him imploringly through the glass as he resumes his breakfast.

'That cat is absolutely wicked, just look at the smile on her face!' Pam laughs, as Graham gets up for the umpteenth time.

I was playing this game, and was about to complete my third circuit, when I noticed Pam taking the washing to the utility room via the broad gravel walk at the rear of the house. I like to be with her when she does her various chores, chatting to her all the time, but that morning I heard her talking to someone in the tone of voice that she usually reserves for me. I was curious because I was behind her and she could not possibly have known I was there.

A moment later, I was astounded to see a handsome male seal-point Siamese inside the utility room. My heart gave a leap and I felt quite faint, believing that Ben had somehow managed to find me after so many years. He had promised that he would never forget me and I had often imagined what it would be like to meet him again, but I was totally unprepared for this encounter. I froze with horror when he turned to face me and I realised that it was not Ben; my disappointment quickly turned to fury and I sprang at him, trying to grab him by the scruff of the neck.

'Let go of him Tia, you'll hurt him.' cried Pam as she tried to wrench me off, only succeeding after one or two abortive attempts.

I am ashamed to admit that I behaved abominably—swearing, growling and trying to bite him. He, I must say, behaved like a perfect gentleman and did not attempt to retaliate.

Graham had by then left for Palma, knowing nothing about the intruder who was causing such disruption to the tranquil routine of the household. Pam shut the handsome stranger in the utility room and carried me back to the house, still screaming and swearing with my tail in its flue-brush mode. She prepared food and water for the visitor and took it to him—leaving me pacing the floor and hammering at the windows in an attempt to escape and see what was going on.

'Tia stop that noise for heaven's sake; you're behaving like an alley cat,' Pam said, when she returned. 'Be quiet while I telephone the vet to ask him whether he knows of anyone who has lost a male seal-point Siamese.'

This was too much for me and I jumped on to her lap, pushed my face against the mouthpiece and screeched into the telephone. The terrible racket astonished the vet at the other end of the line as I continued to wail.

'Oh no,' said Pam, 'that's not him, that's Tia—she's gone berserk because her territory has been invaded!'

The vet promised that he would make enquiries; several of his clients had Siamese toms and he would try to discover whether one was missing.

Pam knew that she could not keep me apart from the intruder for long, as I was determined to tear him to pieces. She contacted some friends she knew to be cat lovers, who lived down the road, and they eagerly agreed to have him, even though she stressed that the rightful owner might turn up at any time.

Thank goodness, I thought, we could now return to normal and Pam had not even considered adopting him—that would have been unbearable.

When Graham returned, Pam told him what had happened and he looked at me reproachfully.

'Tia, how could you behave so badly? You're usually such a sweet and gentle cat—I'm absolutely disgusted.'

I wondered what he would have done if someone had invaded his domain!

About nine o'clock that evening, the telephone rang and Pam picked up the receiver. Someone was obviously speaking rapidly in Spanish, because I heard her trying to reply despite her still rather inadequate command of the language. I knew that it concerned our intruder when she turned to Graham and said:

'That was a young Spanish girl living in the village who lost her male seal-point Siamese four days ago. I'm sure the cat is hers because, when I questioned her, she told me that his name was Rubi and that he was a tom. I've promised that we'll return him to her within half-an-hour. However, we must first get him back from the Pattersons down the road.'

'I'll ring, while you get the basket ready,' said Graham. This he did, but as soon as he put down the telephone, he turned to Pam.

'Oh dear, they were not over-enthusiastic about handing him back. Apparently, he's settled in very well; moreover their dog has taken to him and the two of them are already firm friends.'

'I did explain this morning that the owner might claim the cat,' said Pam. 'Come on, we must go and get him.'

They set off down the hill in the car with my travelling basket on board. Later, I heard how Mr Rubi was extracted from the Pattersons, who were very reluctant to part with him, and taken down to the village where the young girl was overjoyed to be reunited with her cat.

When they returned, they left the empty basket outside the garage door. Next morning, I spent some time sniffing at it with the fur on my back bristling and my ears pinned back as I picked up the stranger's scent—Graham would have to wash it out thoroughly before I consented to travel in it again!

We soon recovered from the unexpected arrival and departure of Mr Rubi and I wandered down the hill to tell Josephine all about it. I soon found her, sitting in our usual meeting place.

'Hello, I was beginning to wonder what had happened to you.'

'You may well ask,' I said. 'We had an intruder, a male seal-point Siamese, who had walked up from the village. It apparently took him four days and he thought that he was in heaven when he got to our house.'

'Why do you say that?' questioned Josephine.

'Because I caught him with his front paws round Pam's neck trying to give her love bites. He'd jumped up on top of the washing machine, almost level with her waist, and was attempting to climb up her. I've never heard anyone purr so loudly and he was rubbing his face all over her. Mind you, I could tell she was scared to death and she deliberately avoided mentioning his amorous attack to Graham.'

'My goodness! What happened next?'

'I'm afraid I created quite a scene; part of my anger was due to frustration and disappointment because, for one split second, I thought that Ben had come to find me.'

'Did you fight?'

'Well, I leaped up on to the washing machine and tried to grab him round the neck, but Pam pulled me off before I got a firm hold.'

'Oh dear, it must have been awful.'

'Yes it was. Pam shut me in the house while she fed him and gave him some water and then took him to some people down the road—I believe they live opposite you—and I never saw or heard of him again.'

'What an experience,' cried Josephine. 'You certainly lead an exciting life!'

I had to agree with her observation.

# 19. Visitors

Life was sweet in Mallorca and we lived it to the full. Pam and Graham had many friends who came to stay—all of them eager to see why we had left our comfortable house in England to emigrate to a foreign country. Since these visitors were nearly all cat lovers, I would accompany them round the garden bounding ahead of them and waiting for them to catch up with me before leading them to another interesting feature. At the end of the tour, they usually commented on how helpful I had been and either Pam or Graham would pick me up and hug me.

Other friends had holiday homes in Mallorca and came over regularly two or three times a year. When they arrived, we would often throw a party and, although I was sometimes nervous when there were many people laughing and joking at the same time, I soon learned that if I greeted each guest in turn I would be given a stroke and surreptitiously slipped a tasty morsel from the tray of *tapas*.

Pam and Graham entertained frequently and some of their guests were strangers to me; lunches were no problem because I could always wander down the garden or visit Josephine, but dinners, particularly in the winter, caused an unwelcome disruption to my routine and I usually remained in my basket or hid in the utility room.

These evenings were very boring and I was relieved when I heard sounds of departure; but I endured them as best I could, because Pam and Graham were obviously enjoying themselves. Any guests who lingered needed some form of motivation to leave; otherwise, none of us would have been able to settle for the night. I experimented with many different methods and found the most effective way was to approach the assembled group and interrupt their conversation with a couple of loud banshees. This inevitably stopped them in midstream, possibly because they had never heard anything like it before, and they would immediately rise and make a hurried exit—exclaiming that they had not realised how late it was.

I abhorred one particular guest who came to our house frequently but was definitely not a cat lover—once being indiscreet enough to describe at length the sadistic method by which he would like to dispose of all felines. After I heard this horrifying narrative, I gave him a wide berth and was very surprised that Pam and Graham did not do the same. I believe they thought he was joking but I knew he was not. Long after all the other guests had gone, he would sit drinking Graham's best whisky until around two in the morning, waiting for his favourite night club to warm up—and would only take his leave when he felt that the time had come for him to grace its portals with his presence.

I sensed his hatred of cats and would delay joining Pam and Graham until it got so late that I could no longer bear to be apart from them. Usually, they would be sitting on the sofa together, facing their guest; I would jump up and settle between them, my body pressed closely against theirs for added security, and the three of us would yawn simultaneously at intervals in an abortive attempt to hasten his departure. Fortunately, the friendship did not last and he was eventually dropped from their guest list.

When they were not entertaining at home, Pam and Graham liked to eat at one of their favourite restaurants, most of which served such generous portions that Pam would take a doggy bag in which to bring back any surplus for me to sample. In this way, I have enjoyed *cabrito*, *chateaubriand*, *coq au vin*, *lechona* and *lomo de cerdo* from many of the best establishments on the island.

On one occasion, I invited Josephine to join me for dinner because we had a surfeit of roast lamb.

Josephine followed me home and Pam greeted the two of us as we arrived at the kitchen door.

'Ah! There you are Tia, I see you've brought Josephine with you. I was about to prepare your meal; bring Josephine in—I'm sure she'd like some too.'

'Where has all this meat come from?' asked Josephine between mouthfuls, while we were both eating our fill.

'Well, last night Pam and Graham returned from Ciro's with two almost complete legs of lamb,' I replied. 'This morning I overheard her telling a friend that the restaurant was so crowded and the tables so close together that she couldn't help observing a young couple sitting alongside. When the waiter brought them two huge portions of lamb, they could only pick at them because they had struggled through an immense starter. Pam noticed their quandary and, knowing how much I love roast lamb, asked whether they intended to eat it. Graham was furious with her for speaking to them—in case they thought she wanted it for herself.'

'What happened then?' asked Josephine.

'Well, when Pam told them that it was for her Siamese cat, they were only too happy to pass their plates across. They had eaten an enormous lunch that day and the substantial starter had been much larger than they anticipated. They were amused when Carlos, *el mayordomo*, put chunks of their meat into aluminium foil—identifying the days for which they would provide me with meals by saying: *'lunes, martes, miércoles...'*

'Their loss is our gain,' said Josephine. 'I'm really enjoying this—you're lucky to be having it for the rest of the week.'

Carlos was eager to meet the cat that appreciated his restaurant's fine cuisine; Pam promised to bring me down to be introduced at a quiet time before the busy lunch period.

As I was carried in, wearing my best collar and lead, several waiters dressed like penguins in long aprons, were standing in line waiting to greet me; they bowed when I extended a paw to each of them in turn—as if I were royalty. I was then taken over to a large fish tank where several lobsters were clambering languidly over stones while some corpulent fish swam above them. The bubbles of air, which rose constantly from the base of the tank, fascinated me and I watched happily until Carlos appeared—wearing a dark suit and clutching a red leather-covered menu.

'Good morning Tia, I'm delighted to meet you at last,' he said. Then, with a mischievous wink at Pam, he opened the menu with a flourish and continued: 'What would madam like today—may I suggest a little smoked salmon followed by a nice piece of *solomillo*?'

'I'm sure she'd love that,' said Pam enthusiastically.

He turned and whispered to a waiter who departed for the kitchen, returning a few minutes later with two small parcels wrapped in aluminium foil, which he handed to Carlos.

'These are especially for you, Tia. ¡*Que aproveche*! Enjoy your meal!' he said as he gave them to Pam—while I expressed my gratitude by purring loudly and nudging his hand with my nose.

A week or two later, Pam and Graham had a little free time and set off in the car to explore the northern part of the island. Pam was holding an interesting package when I went to the door to greet them on their return. As she swept me into her arms, she said:

'Look what I've brought back for you Tia—it's a lovely piece of the *paletilla de cordero* I had for lunch. You'll never guess who was at the same restaurant. Do you remember the Wilsons—Sapphire's family? Well, they were sitting quite near us and we had a long conversation with them. They've now come to live permanently over here in Puerto Pollença; we've invited them to visit us next week and to bring Sapphire with them.'

I was astonished and could hardly contain my excitement at the thought of seeing Sapphire after such a long time. I waited impatiently until, finally, an unfamiliar car arrived and I saw her peering out of the back window, looking as beautiful as ever. We greeted one another effusively and wandered off together to find a quiet spot to exchange our news.

'How long have you been living over here?' I asked.

'Only a few weeks; my family sold their holiday apartment and bought an old house near the sea at Puerto Pollença when Ken retired.'

'Did you enjoy the flight?' I asked Sapphire as we stretched out comfortably in the warm sunshine.

'No, it was dreadful. I was put into a large plastic container and travelled with some other miserable animals in the hold; it seemed ages before I was collected from the carousel at Palma airport.'

'I was lucky, Pam arranged for me to travel with her in the cabin and I had smoked salmon for lunch.'

'How fortunate! I adore smoked salmon.'

'Quite a lot has happened to me since I last saw you. Did you know that my beautiful Ziggy was knocked down by a car and he died just before we were due to come out here?'

'No, I didn't, I'm so sorry. What a terrible tragedy; he was such a lovely boy. I can remember him exercising with Charles when we occupied neighbouring pens at the cattery. Did you know that I was there when it caught fire and burned to the ground a couple of years ago?'

'No, how dreadful! What happened?' I asked.

'Well, late one night, I thought I could smell smoke and ran into my pen to investigate. A pile of straw in the yard was burning fiercely and the wind was blowing the flames towards our huts; one of which was already well alight. Thankfully, the dogs started barking and woke the owner who ran out in her dressing gown; she was soon joined by some of the neighbours and they all worked desperately hard to save us.

Several cats were so terrified that they wouldn't come out into their pens when they were called, which greatly delayed the helpers; my shed was well alight before I was rescued. I crouched down as low as possible in my pen trying to keep below the smoke, while behind me I heard the sound of glass exploding and flames crackling inside the wooden structure as it caught fire. I was petrified by the time someone unlocked the gate of my pen and bundled me into a basket; I don't know to whom it belonged, but it certainly wasn't mine and it had a horrible smell!

We were taken to the main house and saw the fire increase in intensity, consuming all of the sheds. By then, everyone had been evacuated and, as far as I'm aware, there were no casualties. When the fire brigade eventually arrived there was little left of the cattery; fortunately, the dogs were not affected as their kennels were untouched. Several of the helpers were very brave and risked their lives to save us.

A neighbouring farmer offered his large barn to the owner of the cattery as temporary accommodation and we were moved there—still in the baskets in which we had been rescued. In the morning, workmen quickly erected temporary pens for those of us who couldn't be collected immediately—I was there for another three days before my family returned from Mallorca.'

'What a frightening experience; did your family find somewhere else for you to stay?' I asked.

'Yes, the next time they went abroad, they arranged for me to go to the cattery where I was mated and it was there that I saw Ben again.'

My heart started to pound when she mentioned my lover. 'Did you have a chance to talk to him?' I gasped.

'Yes, but only once, and very briefly. It was when I was being carried from my pen to the office and I spoke to him as I passed his run. He remembered me and assured me that he was well, but I'm sorry that I didn't have time to mention you.'

I was delighted to know that Ben was still alive but frustrated by the lack of any additional information. Sapphire had been my only link with Ben and there was so much that I wanted to know about him. Now that she was living on the island, it was unlikely that I would ever have any more news of him.

To distract myself from thinking about Ben, I suggested a walk down the hill to meet Josephine. I had warned Sapphire about the feral cats but there was no sign of them, although a curious noise that we could not identify made us stop to listen more intently. It sounded like someone rolling a coconut shell down the rocky slope a little to our left; we soon realised that there were two distinct versions of the same sound—one much louder than the other.

We walked over to investigate and arrived in time to see what looked like a large brown stone fall from a rocky ledge on to the grass below, closely followed by a similar but smaller stone. To our amazement, a head suddenly appeared from under each of these objects and small legs began to propel them to the edge of the next shelf, where the process was repeated and they tumbled over, landing with hollow clonks. Neither of us had seen a tortoise before and we could not resist snuffing at their shells in a vain attempt to encourage them to move, but they kept their heads and legs well retracted. After a while, we became bored and left them to continue their unusual progress down the hill. Since then, I have frequently encountered a tortoise when walking on the mountain and sometimes I've even seen one in the garden.

Josephine was delighted to meet Sapphire, having heard me talk about her so often. I thought how elegant the three of us must have looked as we sat there—all Siamese and

# Visitors

yet so different; Josephine with her dark seal-point coat, Sapphire with much paler fur edged with lilac blue and me with my chocolate and cream colouring.

'Do you like living in Mallorca?' Josephine asked Sapphire after the usual introductions.

'I'm sure that I will, and it's great to have Tia living here too, but just at present our house is being restored and I spend most of my time evading the building work,' replied Sapphire.

'I know what that's like,' said Josephine, 'A year or so ago, the old house where I live was completely rebuilt and considerably extended. We had almost continuous noise for months, the worst offender being the chipper-hammer that was used to cut the foundations; my teeth rattled for weeks with the vibration of that horrible machine.'

'With us, it's tile-cutting,' sighed Sapphire. 'They're laying a new terrace and, at frequent intervals, a disk cutter screams as it bites into the tiles. They don't realise how sensitive cats are to noise and, what with the cutter, their loud radio and constant hammering from the carpentry work, I'm nearly going crazy.'

'It will end soon,' I reassured her. 'They build very efficiently in Mallorca so things are usually done quite quickly, but I agree that the noise can be terrible. They drilled for water near us and my head buzzed for weeks from the sound of the borer.'

Josephine walked part of the way back with us and then bade us farewell, as it was almost time for her evening meal. We arrived home to find preparations in hand for the Wilsons to leave.

'There you are,' said Joan. 'We were just about to call you.'

As they prepared for their departure, the Wilsons thanked Pam and Graham for a lovely day and expressed the hope that they would be able to visit them in their new house soon. Since I had evidently enjoyed my reunion with Sapphire, I was included in the invitation. I watched her hop on to the parcel shelf at the back of their car and settle for the long journey to the other side of the island. As she disappeared from view, I was already starting to miss her, but at least I could look forward to our return visit.

# 20. The Doberman

When Pam and Graham were going out for the evening, they always ensured that I had a place of refuge by leaving the cat-flap to the utility room open if I had not returned before they left the house. On one unforgettable occasion, they were going to a dinner dance at a restaurant some distance away. I heard them calling me and immediately turned towards the house, but was only half way home when I saw the tail-lights of their car disappearing round a bend as it descended the hill. Rather despondently, knowing that I would be spending the evening alone in the utility room, I continued my trek to the house. Suddenly, I became aware of something rapidly approaching me from behind and, on turning my head, saw to my horror that a Doberman had scented me and was racing towards me— one bite from its vicious jaws would have been enough to kill me.

I pinned back my ears, darted towards a tall pine tree immediately ahead of me and scrambled up the trunk until I was well out of the dog's reach. I could almost feel its panting breath as it stood on its hind legs and stretched up trying to get at me. When this failed, it began to spring at the tree growling and barking in a frenzied attempt to reach me. The fur on my back rose with fear and I continued to climb higher until the ground was far below.

# The Doberman

The Doberman sat at the base of the tree for what seemed like hours—hoping that I would come down or fall off the branch to which I was precariously clinging. When it grew dark, I could no longer see the dog but I sensed that it was still there—watching and waiting. Later, I heard a voice further down the hill calling:

'Butch, Butch, come here at once!'

With a final snarl, it moved off and then I heard its owner greeting it in the distance. I sat motionless for a little longer, in case it decided to return, before I started to descend. My muscles were stiff and cramped but I was unable to stretch since that would have involved standing on three legs—creating an additional danger of overbalancing and falling. As with the loft ladder, I discovered that it was much easier to ascend than climb down. Freeing my claws from the rough bark of the tree was very difficult; a sharp tug could have sent me hurtling downwards and I had to extract them slowly and carefully. Because of the height, I began to feel dizzy and lost my nerve, but I managed to scramble on to a branch and sit wedged against the trunk, bracing myself against a strengthening north-east wind.

It must have been around two in the morning before I heard the sound of Pam and Graham's car. I watched with despair as it continued up the hill and I realised that they could not possibly have seen me up in the pine tree. When they did not find me waiting for them in front of the house, or in the utility room, I knew that they would start searching for me.

I was right; I soon heard Graham's voice calling, because the wind was blowing from his direction and the tree is not very far from the house as the crow flies— although it is quite a distance down the winding road. My frantic cries in reply drifted away in the wind and I began to panic, wondering how much longer I could cling to the branch.

Tired, hungry, thirsty and almost at the point of despair, I became aware of a light swaying from side to side as it progressed slowly down the hill towards me. It stopped almost at the base of the tree and I could just make out Graham's shape as he called my name again. I gathered all my strength to answer him and he beamed his torch upwards, until its light was reflected by my eyes.

'There you are Tia!' he cried. 'How on earth did you get up there? Thank goodness I've found you—we've been calling for ages and thought that we'd lost you again.'

Then, to my dismay, he turned and started to walk away. I cried my loudest in an attempt to bring him back but he continued up the hill and I heard him calling to Pam:

'I've found her! She's in that tall pine tree on the corner near the white house. I've spoken to her but we'll need the extending ladder to reach her because she's very high up.'

The moon came out from behind a cloud, illuminating the pair of them in full evening dress, carrying a metal ladder, which glinted in the moonlight as they walked down the hill—looking like Raffles and his friend setting out to burgle a country house. On reaching the tree, they propped the ladder against the trunk and extended it to its maximum length.

'I'm sorry, I can't go that far up because I get vertigo at that height,' said Graham.

'That's great!' said Pam, 'I wish you'd told me that before and I would have changed out of this long dress.'

I could hear the noise of her dainty high-heeled shoes scraping on the rungs of the ladder as she climbed up.

However, even when she neared the top, she couldn't quite reach me.

'Come Tia, come closer!'

I could not move and started to cry. So near and yet so far! Although she could see that there was a sheer drop down the mountainside beyond the tree, Pam would not give in. She mounted one more rung, even though it meant that she could no longer hold on to the top of the ladder and had to balance with her body pressed against the trunk, clinging to it as best she could.

'Be careful!' Graham called up from below as he steadied the base of the ladder to prevent it from twisting or slipping.

Pam clutched the bark of the tree with her left hand and, with her right arm extended to its limit, she just managed to lift me by my left front leg and shoulder; I hung in the air precariously until she bent her arm and clasped me against her chest. By then, she was physically and mentally exhausted and had to pause for a moment before inching her way down the ladder and collapsing into Graham's arms—the three of us clinging together and trembling with relief.

On feeling firm ground beneath my paws, I cautiously stretched my cramped limbs and climbed home via a short cut up the mountainside, while they walked along the road carrying the ladder. By the time they arrived, I was sitting on the doormat waiting to greet them and, after I had drunk some water and eaten a morsel of chicken, I settled thankfully in my basket while they went belatedly to bed—all of us traumatised by our experience. I often wonder whether they knew that the awful Doberman had chased me or whether they thought I had climbed the tree for fun!

The Doberman was not my only enemy; periodically I caught a glimpse of the group of feral cats that Josephine had mentioned. They lived somewhere on the mountainside but only occasionally ventured in our direction; there were five or six in the gang, led by the terrible Bruno.

After dinner one evening, we were sitting comfortably in the *salón* reading and talking. It was dark, but the *persianas* were open and the outside lights illuminated the terrace. Suddenly, I was aware of being watched and I turned my head to see Bruno making faces at me through the glazed door. I sprang up immediately and raced towards him, growling and wailing, with my fur standing on my back in a ridge and my tail in angry flue-brush mode. I battered on the door with my front paws while he cheekily strutted up and down in front of me; then I watched aghast as he purposefully backed up against one of the chairs on the terrace and, with his tail upright and quivering, he sprayed it. I saw the rest of the gang hiding behind one of the large plant pots, tittering and laughing as he carried out this ultimate insult.

By the time Pam and Graham had reached the door and peered out, there was no one in sight. Graham went out on to the terrace and, turning to me, said:

'There's no one there now, Tia. Calm down, I'll shut the *persianas* and draw the curtains so that you won't be able to see anything that may be lurking outside.'

I felt better once the curtains had been drawn and settled down for the rest of the evening because, even if Bruno returned, he would be unable to make faces at me.

Sometimes, when I was home alone, the gang would return and race around the garden, howling and swearing as they went, attacking the flower beds and scooping the earth on to the gravel paths, leaving their calling cards on the terrace when they departed. I was powerless to prevent this desecration of our property, and it infuriated me to think that Pam and Graham would have to spend a considerable amount of time and energy repairing the damage caused by the vandalism. A smell of disinfectant permeated the air for several hours after the mess had been cleaned up, making it impossible to enjoy the pleasure of relaxing on the terrace—these invasions by the marauding band always left me in a state of nervous exhaustion. When we next met, I told Josephine what Bruno and his mob had been doing and asked her whether her home had ever been similarly defiled.

'No,' she replied. 'They wouldn't dare approach our house because, if our dogs were off their chains for exercise, they would make short work of a bunch of underfed feral cats. Anyway, I expect they like to taunt you because they probably think you're rather snooty.'

'I'm not snooty,' I retorted, 'but I do maintain certain standards.'

'Yes, I know and you're to be commended. However, I imagine that they're very jealous of you, even though they would never be able to adjust to a lifestyle like yours. The problem is that the people across the road still feed them and are now trying to tame them. It's quite ridiculous really as they'll never be tamed—they don't want to be,' replied Josephine.

'Many years ago, when I lived in England, I escaped one morning and was befriended by a feral cat called Mitzi, who was very kind and anxious to help me start a new life. Unfortunately, I couldn't face her harsh existence and the thought of actually eating food from dustbins made me heave. She thought nothing of it because it had become her way of life and she wouldn't have wanted to exchange it for mine. I was actually relieved when my owner found me and took me home after only a few hours of freedom.'

The two of us were walking side by side while we talked—rather like two elegant ladies on a Sunday walk down the *Paseo Borne* in Palma. However, our promenade was short-lived, as we suddenly became aware of a dozen unfriendly feline eyes watching us and Josephine cried:

'They've spotted us. I didn't think they were around at the moment; shall we fight or shall we run?'

'Let's run!' I said.

# The Doberman

# 21. Bruno Meets his Match

On cool days, one of my favourite places to be warm and comfortable is under the coverlet of a bed in the guest room. I have learned how to lift it at the pillow end, squeeze under it and curl up on the lambswool under blanket—leaving the bed virtually undisturbed.

Graham likes to know where I am and frequently checks the house to see where I have settled. At first, when he came into the bedroom, he would think it was empty, but before long he discovered my hiding place. Now, he looks for the tell-tale bump, as I lie hidden under the coverlet and gently calls me. I keep quiet and still for as long as I can, hoping that he will leave me undisturbed, but sometimes I feel him turn back the bedspread and see his face smiling down at me.

If I am very warm and comfortable, I look at him pleadingly and he usually replaces the cover, allowing me to slumber in peace. Pam also knows where I like to curl up but she has a hang-up about hygiene and is not too happy about my sleeping in the spare bed. If she finds me, no amount of pleading glances will prevent her from plucking me out of my warm nest.

After I have rested, I like to find a warm spot where I can sit and watch some activity. If it is a fine day there are many suitable places in the garden where I can be comfortable and undisturbed, but on cold days the house offers fewer choices. I need somewhere that provides me with a good view of Pam or Graham as they work, but sufficiently out of their way to avoid being moved.

There used to be three white Royal Doulton ornaments on the sideboard; a seal, a bird and a goat, but one day, as we all sat in the *salón*, we heard a tremendous crash in the adjoining room. When Graham dashed in to see what had happened, he found that a cord supporting a heavy painting had broken and the picture had fallen directly on to the porcelain goat, shattering it beyond repair. This created a vacant spot between the two remaining ornaments, which was bathed in sunlight by the middle of the morning. I found it easy to leap up, pick my way delicately between the seal and the bird and sit enjoying the warmth of the sun on my fur while watching Pam at work through the open door to the kitchen.

I was relaxing on the sideboard one morning when Graham walked into the room calling my name. He was standing quite close to me and I saw no need to reply but, when he looked straight at me without even noticing me, I realised that he had become so accustomed to seeing three white figurines on the sideboard that he did not recognise the replacement. He continued his search and must have walked by me five or six times before I took pity on him and spoke. He jumped when he heard my voice so close to him, but soon saw the funny side of the incident and fetched Pam to admire her new ornament.

Pam and Graham have made many visits to the UK during the last thirteen years. Before they leave, they still carefully remove any porcelain within my reach because, when I was younger, I used to get bored and could not resist the temptation to jump on to the furniture, dislodging any objects in my path—unfortunately, Lladro figurines have no chance of survival if they fall on to a marble floor. Once everything breakable has been packed away, I am given the run of the house during their absence.

Carmen, my friend next door, comes in twice a day to look after me. As she enters the house, she calls my name softly, which gives me time to get out of my basket and make my way to the door to greet her. She is always kind and makes a tremendous fuss of me—gently picking me up and holding me close while whispering *guapa* in my ear. Then follows a *régimen* to which she strictly adheres; first she feeds me and changes my water, then we go through to the *salón* where I sit in the middle of the carpet while she grooms me, and finally we go out for a breath of fresh air. While we patrol the grounds together, I usually walk beside her on my collar and lead but, if there is even a hint of a cold wind, she carefully wraps me in the quilt from my basket and carries me round.

For some time, Carmen was in poor health and she underwent a major operation. This coincided with an important family event in the UK, which Pam and Graham wanted to attend, so they had to find an alternative cat-sitter to look after me. Fortunately, a German couple, who live across the road with their two Schnauzers, are also cat lovers. Eleanora, the wife, kindly offered to stand in for Carmen until she recovered. I was somewhat apprehensive because Eleanora is the complete opposite to Carmen and stands well over six feet tall—even towering above Graham. From our garden, we can hear her booming voice as she talks to her dogs in strident German, and her excitable disposition contrasts with Carmen's calmness.

The first time Eleanora burst into the house, following Pam and Graham's departure for England, everything seemed to shake as she strode towards the kitchen and I cowered in my basket; so terrified that my tail immediately went into flue-brush mode and the fur on my back formed a vertical ridge. I cringed as she reached down into my bed and scooped me up with her two huge hands. She then hugged me closely, while vigorously stroking my head and deafening me with cries of '*liebchen, liebchen.*'

I soon discovered that she had a heart of gold. Pam had left small tins of gourmet cat food for me, clearly marked for each day, but Eleanora considered them too monotonous and totally inadequate; they were supplemented by extra meals of liver, kidney and heart, which she cooked specially for me. I was initially very suspicious of this unfamiliar fare and stalked the plate, approaching it from several directions before venturing to taste it; but I soon found that it was so delicious that I jeopardised my figure by eating every scrap.

Eleanora and I became firm friends and I even came to an understanding with her two fierce Schnauzers. Initially they went wild whenever they caught a glimpse of me and would rush to the gate, pushing their heads through the bars and barking furiously, until she dragged them away saying: '*Es una amiga.*' She usually spoke to them in German but, on this occasion, she used Spanish for my benefit. They did not fully accept me but, knowing that I was a friend of the family, they looked the other way and pretended they had not seen me when I entered their garden. At that time I had no idea how greatly I would come to value their co-operation.

The feral cats became bolder and more of a nuisance; they were too frightened to attack me in our grounds but started to follow me whenever I went outside, taunting me in coarse voices and threatening to tear me apart. Bruno was the worst, leering at me and bragging about what he would do to me if he ever caught me—so I devised a plan to teach Bruno and his gang a lesson.

One evening, when returning home after visiting Josephine, I sensed that the gang was watching me; a flood of abusive language soon confirmed this. Knowing that they would immediately give chase, I ran up the hill and through a small gate at the bottom of Eleanora's garden, with the whole pack pursuing me. I raced across her grounds and out through the main gates, while Bruno and his friends, screeching at the top of their voices, found themselves face to face with two irate Schnauzers—who had tolerated my use of their garden as a short cut but were not prepared to overlook an invasion by a gang of mangy mogs. Battle raged and fur flew in all directions as Bruno and his gang frantically attempted to escape from my trap. The wall near our gate provided me with a perfect vantage point and I watched, unable to stem the self-satisfied smirk on my face, as the dogs dealt with my persecutors.

A few days later, when I heard Gregoria's car coming up the drive, I decided to evade the noise of her vacuum and saunter down the hill to see Josephine and tell her what had happened. I found her under her favourite bush and immediately saw that she was bursting to impart some information of her own.

'*Hola* Tia!' she exclaimed. 'Did you know that Bruno and his mob have gone away?'

'No, I didn't—what happened?'

'Well, the people who used to put food out for them have sold their house and returned to Belgium. In any case, I think that Bruno had an accident of some kind; he was limping badly when I last saw him,' answered Josephine.

'I was going to tell you about that. All of the gang suffered at least one injury when they were stupid enough to follow me as I led them into the garden where the Schnauzers live.'

'Oh Tia, how cunning of you! I'm sure that was the real reason why they left in such a hurry. Thank goodness we'll no longer have to watch out for them every time we meet.'

After a while, I left Josephine and walked home happily, revelling in the knowledge that Bruno and his mob would not ambush me.

# 22. A House by the Sea

Not long after the incident with Bruno and his gang, Pam had a call from the Wilsons inviting us to spend a day with them at the old *finca* they had recently bought in Puerto Pollença; I could not wait to see Sapphire again and visit her new home.

I watched eagerly for signs of preparation for the journey and suspected that it might be imminent when I saw Graham washing and polishing the car, which was dark blue—a choice of colour that he quickly regretted when he discovered that every speck of dust was clearly visible. When he had finished, it sparkled from end to end and I could see myself clearly reflected in the dark finish. I climbed on to its roof in order to enjoy the last rays of the sun, which were warming the metal, and found to my horror that I had left a trail of perfect paw prints behind me. Unless it suddenly poured with rain, Graham would have no difficulty in identifying the guilty party—but the sky was clear and there was little chance of that happening. Had I been human, a brief wipe with a duster would soon have removed the tell-tale evidence—at times like these I realise my limitations, paws are no substitute for hands. I could have given the marks a few quick flicks with my tail had it been in flue-brush mode, but there was nothing to frighten me and I could not make it fluff out to order. I just had to hope that Graham would absent-mindedly get in and drive off without noticing.

The following day Graham loaded the car, so preoccupied with ensuring that nothing essential was left behind that he never even glanced at the roof. I came as soon as I was called and jumped straight on to the back seat, determined to be on my best behaviour. We set off for the two-hour journey and, by clambering on to the parcel shelf, I had an excellent view of the unfamiliar scenery on either side of the old Roman road to Alcudia.

Pam and Graham were relaxed and chatted to one another as we headed north-east.

'What a pity so many of the windmills are now derelict,' remarked Pam—commenting on the remnants of old Mallorca, which we could see as we crossed the flat *pla*.

'Yes,' agreed Graham. 'They've become victims of progress and are now superseded by electric pumps as a means of raising water for irrigation, but a society has been formed to preserve them—over on the right, there's a fine example of one that's been restored.'

I pressed my face against the window to get a better view, just in time to see a windmill with brightly coloured blue and white sails, looking like the second prize rosette in a cat show.

We turned off the Alcudia road and headed for Puerto Pollença, climbing from the plain up into a range of hills lining the northern coast of the island. Pam unfolded a letter she had received from the Wilsons giving directions on how to find their *finca*. She turned to Graham and said:

'The house seems to be quite near the sea, but the road leading down to it is little more than a track and may be hard to find. Go into the town and take the road to Formentor; after that, I'll try to follow the map they've drawn for us—keep a lookout for a turning on the left just after a small café.'

I realised that we were nearly there, because I had spotted the café long before Pam exclaimed:

'There it is! Turn left here and follow the track down the hill until you see two tall palm trees on the right marking the entrance to the *finca*, which is hidden at the end of a long driveway.'

A few minutes later, we saw the palms flanking some open wrought iron gates and turned into the drive. Before long, we caught our first glimpse of the attractive old stone *finca*, which was partially covered by a huge bougainvillaea bearing hundreds of purple bracts. A wide archway provided access to a shady, stone-flagged courtyard, where a colonnade of pillars supported vines trained along wires to form a living green roof from which bunches of unripe grapes hung in profusion. At the far end, a carved stone crest surmounted an imposing oak doorway with a curved top.

The Wilsons came out to greet us when they heard the sound of our car—Joan was carrying Sapphire but she put her down in order to embrace Pam. I ran to my friend as soon as Graham opened the car door and we pressed our heads together, twitching our tails and rubbing noses in an ecstatic greeting.

Ken then came forward, saying as he shook hands:

'Hello there! We're a bit off the beaten track but once you're here, it's perfect. Just look at those cats—they're obviously delighted to see one another again!'

'Come on in, lunch will be ready soon but would you like to have a look around the garden first,' said Joan.

'Yes. What a heavenly spot! You must be thrilled to have found it,' observed Pam.

As they toured the garden, Sapphire showed me her favourite haunts where she could relax undisturbed while the restoration work was being carried out on the house. Fortunately, as it was Saturday, there were no builders around and everything was tranquil. It was hot and sunny but a soft breeze wafted interesting scents up from the sea, as we stood, side-by-side, snuffing the air and enjoying the cooling wind on our fur.

A table had been laid in the shade on the paved terrace at the rear of the house and we sat nearby, eating our lunch and listening attentively to the conversation, which turned to the reasons why the Wilsons had decided to emigrate.

'While we had the apartment, we only thought of Mallorca as a holiday location but, as soon as we saw this place, we decided that it was where we wanted to live permanently,' said Ken.

'Yes, we love it here,' said Joan. 'We moved just in time because the cattery where Sapphire used to stay, and where we first met you, had a dreadful fire and closed down a few years ago. Since then we've been using the Pinnacle Cattery where Sapphire was mated, but the owner has just been killed in a car accident and the executors have put it up for sale lock, stock and barrel.'

'She used to breed Siamese. What will happen to her cats?' asked Pam.

'So far as I know they'll be disposed of. The site is to be developed and everything must go.'

'What a shame, I've never been there but the name is familiar because it was on Ziggy's pedigree. I assume that's where Tia was mated some years ago, before she came to us,' remarked Pam.

'I believe that Sapphire had some kittens, do you ever hear anything of them?' Graham enquired.

'Yes, several of them have been highly successful at cat shows,' said Joan.

I turned to Sapphire and congratulated her—her enigmatic smile barely disguised her pride.

When we had finished lunch, we were free to wander off until it was time for me to go home. Sapphire suggested, as I was with her, we could make the hazardous journey down to the tiny beach; she was frightened to go alone because nobody would know where to find her if she missed her footing and fell.

I love a little danger and instantly agreed, but I started to regret my decision when she led me to what appeared to be a sheer cliff with the sea lapping against a small patch of sand far below us.

'Come on Tia, it's not too difficult if you follow the path,' said Sapphire as she picked her way downwards.

When we had safely reached the beach, we found it completely deserted; the sand was hot beneath our paws until we neared the edge of the sea where it was cool and damp. It was lovely to dip our toes into the shallow water, as it rippled gently towards us, and we walked the full length of the cove before turning to retrace our steps.

The climb up the cliff was much easier than the descent and we arrived back at the house just as Pam and Graham started to call me. I ran up to them and Pam quickly picked me up and held me as she thanked the Wilsons for a lovely day, ending by saying:

'You must come over to us again and bring Sapphire with you, Tia loves being with her—I'll give you a ring soon.'

On the return journey, I mused over every minute of my day with Sapphire and was happy in the knowledge that I would be seeing her again in the near future. She was fortunate to have such a beautiful home close to the sea, but I decided that I would not like to exchange it for ours as I enjoy living high on the mountain. I could not wait to visit Josephine at the earliest possible opportunity in order to tell her all about our trip to the northern part of the island and my adventures with Sapphire.

We were all tired by the time we arrived home but, after dinner and a relaxed evening together, I was ready for my nightly game with Graham, which has become something of a ritual.

All Siamese love a game before retiring for the night and I am no exception. Graham always allows some time for us to play at bedtime and we have devised a game that is slightly akin to arm wrestling—except it involves his hand and my head.

He kneels on the hearthrug and holds one hand out in front of him, palm outwards. I walk purposefully towards him and push my head firmly against his palm; he then gently cups my head in his hand while twisting his wrist slightly as a starting signal and we commence a battle of wits.

The idea is for me to twist my neck sharply to free my head from his grip; if he relaxes his muscles sufficiently, his limp hand simply follows every movement I make, so I wait until I detect a slight pressure from his fingers and then give my head a sharp twist to break free. If he anticipates my move, his hand just stays in place and I have to resort to my second method of escape. By raising a front leg and pressing it against his arm, I can lever it sideways and sharply jerk my head in the opposite direction, usually resulting in a victory for me.

As soon as I have won a point, I prowl back and forth in front of him purring loudly, until he holds his hand out again and I rush to push my head into it for another round. The noise of my purring gets louder and louder until Pam warns Graham not to get me too excited just before I am due to settle for the night.

Now that I am in my nineteenth year, I am treated like an ageing relative; my bed is warmed in winter by means of a special plastic cushion, which retains heat for several hours after it has been 'cooked' on either side in a microwave oven. The timer makes a pinging noise when the first side is done, to indicate that the cushion should be turned over. I sit nearby and watch patiently, waiting for my modern equivalent of a hot water bottle, but occasionally I have to remind Pam that the pad is only half-baked and she races to the microwave as soon as she hears my complaining howl.

With my increasing age, Pam considers it desirable for me to have a night-light in case I wish to get out of my basket during the night. Not one, but two, are plugged in every evening at bedtime; they give the kitchen a pleasantly subdued glow but, as my eyesight is still perfect, they are totally superfluous.

Pam and Graham talk to me constantly as if I were human; we have been together for so long that we can anticipate one another's every move and there are times when I completely forget that I am feline. We are particularly close at bedtime and, after settling me in my basket, they always wish me a fond goodnight before turning off the light.

When Graham abruptly departed for his mysterious journey to England, promising to return in two days with something for me, I convinced myself that it would be a new basket. Now that I am old, I spend much of the day relaxing in my bed and he must have noticed that it was getting very shabby.

Pam and I enjoyed ourselves in his absence, doing all of the things we liked—dancing together to our favourite tunes and relaxing side by side on a lounger in the shade. The time passed quickly and when he was due home, Pam and I sat listening impatiently for the sound of his car coming up the hill.

'Here he is!' exclaimed Pam excitedly. 'Come on Tia, let's go out and meet him.'

We reached the porch just as his car came through the gate and we could see that he was smiling when he stepped out.

'Did you have a successful trip?'

'Very,' he replied, as he opened the rear door.

I moved forward to get a better look and watched as Graham lifted out a larger version of my old basket. I smiled smugly because I had correctly guessed the nature of his gift, but it seemed exceptionally big and, since my old one was an ideal size for me, I was puzzled.

Graham reached into the car again and this time brought out an IATA travelling box. He handled it so gently that I knew it could not be empty and, for one dreadful moment, I thought that it might contain a kitten. However, an instant's reflection convinced me that he would never foist one on me—he knew that at my age I could not adapt to having a boisterous young cat disrupting my tranquil routine. Graham carefully set the box down on the gravel drive and opened its wire door; I detected a movement

*207*

inside and then a striking male seal-point emerged, blinking in the sunlight.

I could feel my whole body tingling with excitement and my heart pounding in my chest as I stood on the doorstep; I could hardly believe my eyes as the incredibly handsome new arrival walked straight towards me. Overcome with emotion, I rushed forward as he smiled and greeted me.

'Hello Tia,' said Ben.